ORGANIZATION
IN PLANTS

by

W. M. M. BARON
M.A., B.Sc.

Head of the Biology Department, Winchester College

LONDON
EDWARD ARNOLD (PUBLISHERS) LTD

Printed in Great Britain by Richard Clay (The Chaucer Press), Ltd.,
Bungay, Suffolk

From the Preface to the first edition

AT THE present time there is considerable emphasis on the unifying and integration of biology teaching. This has been brought about by the renewed interest in genetics, cytology, evolution, ecology and physiology. It is in these fields of biology that much of the most interesting work of the last decade has been carried out and these are the subjects which are posing some of the most interesting and important problems in science.

Many physiological processes are common to both plants and animals and thus physiology can often be taught truly biologically. Unfortunately animals are more difficult experimental material than plants, particularly in schools, and so it is still usual to teach physiology primarily with plants.

This book is intended to bring plant physiology at an intermediate level up to date, to make use of the post-war advances, knitting the new into the corpus of the older work, and above all, to give the subject an ecological background. Physiological processes make much more sense when considered in relation to the plant in its natural environment *competing* with its neighbours. Some effort must also be made to think of the plant from a genetic and evolutionary point of view, endeavouring to relate the various adaptations, structural and physiological, which it possesses to the selective action of the environment.

It is often felt that each step in a scientific argument should be based on practical results. This is clearly an ideal that cannot always be met; nevertheless, useful practical work has been included in every section as far as possible. These practicals contain full details of procedure, but it must be emphasized that the student should not treat them merely as so many recipes. He must work through them carefully, designing controls where necessary and trying to examine the results critically, whether or not it was the result expected. One will soon learn that the unexpected is often as common as the expected in biology!

Many of the results described in this book have been produced in class-work using the simplest of apparatus. Modern practical work seems often to require expensive apparatus, and although ordinary school apparatus will be sufficient for most of the practical work described, a centrifuge (which can be purchased for about £40) and also a device for stirring and accurate temperature control, will be necessary for some of the practicals.

This book is intended for use in advanced and scholarship work in schools and also in some University courses. It is hoped that it will stimulate interest in physiology as well as in ecology and other fields of biology.

January, 1963   W. M. M. Baron

Preface to the second edition

IN the three years since the first edition was published a remarkable change has taken place in biology teaching. Partly as a result of the work of the Nuffield Biology project there is now far greater emphasis on practical work in school biology and in particular the design of experimental work and the drawing of proper deductions. Physiology and ecology are now receiving more attention than formerly and so the material in this book is particularly relevant to modern biology teaching.

In this edition several alterations and corrections have been made. A few sections have been rewritten; notably parts of the Water Relations chapter, and also the introduction to Photosynthesis, which is now treated more fully. On the experimental side there are again a number of additions and corrections. One or two experiments have been cut out or extensively modified, and the section on Chromatography rewritten to include work on thin-layer chromatography. An important section on the use of radioactive carbon dioxide is also included.

W. M. M. Baron

Winchester, April, 1966.

Acknowledgments

I must express my extreme gratitude to Dr. V. S. Butt of the Dept. of Botany, Oxford University, for his constant advice, criticism and fertility of ideas. Dr. B. E. Juniper and Mr. A. E. Greenwood have kindly allowed me to make use of a number of electron microscope photographs, several of which have not been previously published. Dr. R. F. O. Kemp has also given me considerable assistance during the early stages of the preparation of this book.

At Winchester I have been greatly assisted by my colleague, W. H. Dowdeswell, whose wide experience in the teaching of biology has been invaluable. I am also indebted to our laboratory assistants, A. S. Mitchener and A. J. Lewington. Several former students have provided ideas and material and, of course, have had the task of trying out new practical procedures. One of these, J. Pusey, has also helped with the proof reading.

I am also grateful to Mrs. J. H. Preston, who has carried out much of the typing and to the authors and publishers who have allowed me to make use of their material, to whom acknowledgment is made in the text. Finally I would like to thank my publishers for their constant assistance.

Contents

  5   Mineral Nutrition   83

      5.1   Minerals and the soil   83
      5.2   The mineral requirement   84
      5.3   Uptake of minerals   90
      5.4   Mineral transport   95
      5.5   Metabolic utilization of mineral ions   98
      5.6   The nitrogen cycle   99
      5.7   Nitrogen-fixing organisms   101
      5.8   The mechanism of nitrogen fixation   104
      5.9   Some agricultural and horticultural aspects of mineral
            nutrition   105

  6   The Biochemistry of Cell Activities   106

      6.1   Introduction   106
      6.2   The nucleic acids   106
      6.3   Synthesis of amino-acids and polypeptides   115
      6.4   The organization of proteins and enzymes   117
      6.5   Protein synthesis   120
      6.6   Carbohydrate chemistry   124
      6.7   The reserve carbohydrates   126
      6.8   The structural carbohydrates   128
      6.9   The glycosides; the anthocyanins   131
      6.10 Lipid (fat) metabolism   135
      6.11 Integration of cell processes   136

  7   Physiological Organization within the Plant   137

      7.1   Introduction   137
      7.2   The problem of growth and differentiation   137
      7.3   The influence of the environment on growth and
            development   140
      7.4   The effect of light   140
      7.5   The auxins   142
      7.6   The control of flowering   144
      7.7   Other effects of light   149
      7.8   The effect of gravity   149
      7.9   The effect of temperature   150
      7.10 The role of auxins in general metabolism   151

      Appendix A: Experimental Procedures   154

      Appendix B: Useful Reagents   204

      Bibliography   207

      Index   211

1   Introduction : Organization of Cells and Tissues

1.1   Introduction

Plant physiology is a synthesis of many aspects of botany and biology. Its study is based on structure and anatomy on the one hand, and the physical and chemical changes and organization in the whole plant and in its cells on the other. Yet these two lines of approach mean relatively little on their own; they must be related to the environment in which the plant grows and to the evolution of the species concerned. Once it is realized that its various features, at a biochemical, or visible structural level may have important survival value, then physiology takes on a real meaning. It is the aim of this book to show how these aspects: anatomical, physical, chemical or biochemical, genetic and ecological combine and are vital if a plant is to survive in any environment and compete with its neighbours. By studying these factors together it is possible to obtain some understanding of the ways in which plants are organized; in short, of how they work.

1.2   Vital requirements and vital processes

Any wild plant usually occupies a clearly defined ecological niche; it is able to survive there because the site has the environmental conditions that are most favourable, providing it with its various requirements so as to enable it to compete satisfactorily with other plants. What then are these vital requirements?

Perhaps the most obvious of these is the *water requirement*. All living things require water for the hydration of their protoplasm, the living material in their cells. This is largely because the various chemical and physical changes occurring need to take place in a watery medium. The ions, enzymes and organic materials are not able to move about the cell and diffuse to areas where they are required for metabolism, unless the protoplasm is well hydrated. Much of the transport of dissolved material also takes place through water movement, and water is also required in considerable quantity to help maintain the turgidity of the cells and so support the plant, as well as to replace water that has been lost by evaporation.

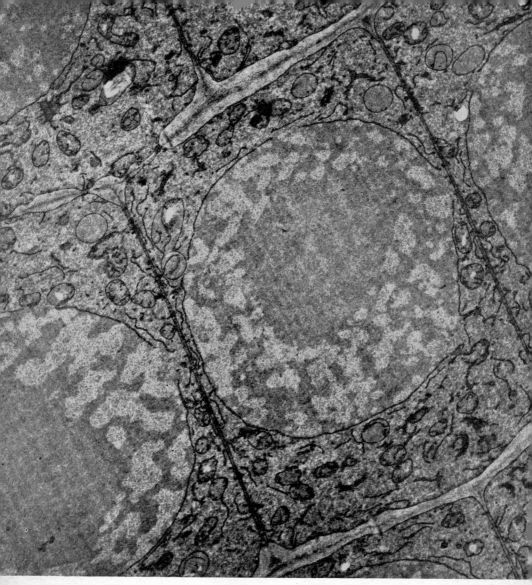

FIG. 1.1A. Meristematic cells of the root apex of barley. (See fig 1.1B opposite.)

An electron-microscope photograph showing details of the structure of the young cell. Note the nucleus with its nucleolus and traces of chromosome material and the nuclear membrane with its occasional gaps. The cytoplasmic particles: the mitochondria, reticulum and ribosomes are also clearly seen. The cell wall is in its early stages of development; the middle lamella has been formed and the primary wall laid down in some areas. (See p. 4 and also Chapters 4 and 6.) (Courtesy of Dr. B. E. Juniper.)

Finally, a rather smaller quantity of water is needed in some chemical reactions, for instance in photosynthesis.

As energy is required for growth, reproduction and the majority of changes going on in the plant, it is vital to possess in the first place a mechanism for obtaining and storing energy, and in the second place, a means for releasing this stored energy for use in the various metabolic processes going on in the plant. Green plants obtain their energy through the process of *photosynthesis*, light being absorbed by the green *chlorophyll* in the *chloroplasts*; *carbon dioxide* is also required and is taken up from the atmosphere. The energy is stored in the form of sugars and reserve or storage

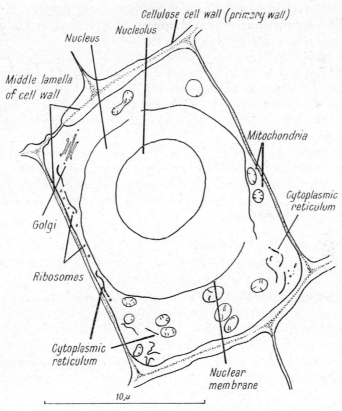

FIG. I.IB. (See fig I.IA opposite.)

carbohydrates. Not all plants have this *light requirement*; some are nongreen and must depend on the organic materials made by green plants for their energy sources; others, the *chemosynthetic* organisms, are totally independent of the sun's energy and use energy released from inorganic changes.

Respiration is the vital process by which the carbohydrates are broken down, usually by an oxidation process requiring atmospheric *oxygen*, to yield energy, which can then be used for the various metabolic processes going on in the plant.

Finally, although plants can obtain the elements that they require for photosynthesis from water in the soil and from carbon dioxide in the air, nevertheless, they need many other elements. For instance, nitrogen is required for the vitally important *proteins*, which, through the organic catalysts, the *enzymes*, are one of the most important groups of organic materials in living things. Nitrogen is seldom utilized by plants in the gaseous state; most of it is taken up from the soil solution in the form of simple inorganic ions, such as nitrate. Other elements such as phosphorus, sulphur, magnesium, copper and iron, are also required for elaboration into various organic molecules, and these too are taken up in the form of inorganic ions; these substances are referred to as the *mineral nutrients*. The fertility of the soil depends to a great extent on the availability of these substances; plant distribution too is closely related to mineral availability, as different plants are differently adapted, and some can tolerate more or less of one mineral than another. Consequently mineral nutrition is another important aspect of physiology.

In this book it is intended to show, first, how and where the vital processes are carried out, particularly within the organization of the basic unit of construction, namely *the cell*, and secondly, something of how these processes are integrated, both one with another and relative to the organization of the plant as a whole.

1.3   The cell as the basic unit

One of the most obvious and in a sense unifying features of plant and animal structure is that the vast majority are composed of cells. True, there are exceptions, notably the slime moulds (*Myxomycetes*) and the coenocytic algae and fungi, which contain many nuclei but no distinct cellular system. But most plants are unicellular or multicellular, and since the time of Schwann in 1839, it has been realized that there must be something about cells which makes them a necessity to the more highly adapted organisms. In higher plants it seems likely that the cell represents the smallest organized mass of material that is capable of fending for itself, of living. Why is this so? The answer to some extent lies in the structure of the cell itself, and for the rest in the organization of the vital processes that go on inside it.

Although there is a great variety of cells, each specialized for a particular function, a simple, relatively unspecialized cell, such as found in the growing region of the root apex, is bounded by (see fig. 1.2A) a thin, elastic cell wall, half of this is composed of the fibrous polysaccharide, cellulose, the rest being mainly packing of hemicellulose polysaccharides and various pectates. This encloses a granular, heterogeneous, watery mass consisting largely of protein, called the *cytoplasm*. Floating in the cytoplasm is the rounded *nucleus*, the controlling unit or 'brain' of the cell. Both the cytoplasm and nucleus are composed largely of protein, they are referred to jointly as the *protoplasm*.

The cell is unable to survive for long without its nucleus. If the nucleus is removed with a micro-manipulator the cell will soon die; if it is replaced it will continue to live. The nucleus is known to contain the inherited factors or *genes* which control the organization of the cell. It seems probable that the nucleus produces various substances which are capable of carrying out diverse reactions in the cytoplasm, and in this way controlling the integration of cell activities.

Observation of the cell under the phase-contrast microscope (which

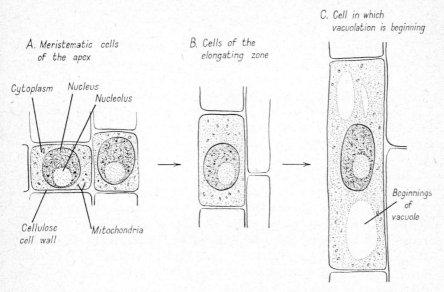

FIG. 1.2. Differentiation in the root tip of the broad bean. ($\times$ 1000.)
The cells shown would all develop into the much elongated xylem elements.

makes the cell structures much clearer without killing the cell and using stains) shows the whole to be in a state of constant motion. This is due to the small particles in the cytoplasm jostling one another partly as a result of the thermal activity of the dissolved ions and molecules hitting the larger particles, a phenomenon known as *Brownian movement*, and partly as a result of metabolically controlled activity called protoplasmic streaming. Careful examination of the granular cytoplasm shows the presence of minute ellipsoid structures called *mitochondria*. These congregate in areas where energy is required and are the sites of respiration. Electron microscope photographs of thin sections of cells show many smaller structures in the cytoplasm (see fig. 1.1.) which may add to the granular appearance of the cell when viewed under an ordinary light microscope.

These smaller structures, the reticulum, ribosomes and Golgi body, can be grouped together as the *microsomal* complement of the cell and are the areas where proteins are synthesized (see p. 120).

1.4 Cell development

There are essentially three phases of cell development; first, *cell division*, second, *extension*, and third, *cell differentiation*. During growth, the cell may gradually differentiate from one division sequence to the next until finally it forms part of a mature tissue which usually contains few dividing cells.

Cell division

Cell division takes place most rapidly in the actively growing areas. As differentiation proceeds, the rate of division usually falls off considerably, though there may be *residual meristems*, for instance the cambium, in which division may continue throughout the life of the plant. The process of division is called *mitosis*; it reveals the presence of rod-like *chromosomes*, composed of protein and nucleic acids, that are known to be the site of the hereditary factors, the genes. Phase-contrast observation or staining techniques (see Appendix, p. 194) show these chromosomes at the onset of cell division as long, thin, double fibres, joined together at the *centromere*. During the division the centromere divides and the two daughter chromosomes are drawn to opposite sides of the cell, where they form two new nuclei. At the end of mitosis these nuclei appear much like the parent nucleus, with no distinct chromosomes visible, but before the next division takes place the cell has synthesized new chromosome material so that they are double once again. In this way mitosis provides each daughter nucleus with a full set of genetic information.

Cell extension

Immature, meristematic cells of the root tip and stem apex are more or less cubical and quite small, perhaps 10–20 μ across (1 μ = 0·001 mm). They are very active metabolically, and rapidly accumulate food materials and synthesize new protoplasm. If older cells farther back are examined (see fig. 1.2C) these will be more elongated, and an additional feature, the vacuole, may be visible. The vacuole is largely composed of water, but contains dissolved mineral and organic materials. It acts as a reservoir for water and minerals; it also keeps the cell inflated and turgid, and in this way, due to one cell pressing against another, helps by giving strength to tissues and support to the whole plant. Finally, the vacuole is important in cell economy. Protoplasm is expensive material; it requires energy for its synthesis and respiration to keep it alive. Water is just the opposite, and a large cell, perhaps simply concerned in giving bulk to a part of the plant, may contain a very large vacuole.

Finally, when the cell reaches its mature size and state of development it may be highly differentiated or specialized according to a particular function. An interesting point is, why is there a maximum size at all? Could not one nucleus control a great mass of protoplasm? The answer seems to be that the size of a fully developed cell (a packing or *parenchymatous* cell may be 100 μ in diameter) is dependent on the ability of the nucleus to control the work of the cell constituents. Materials diffusing out of the nucleus and giving 'instructions' for cell operation may only be capable of moving a limited distance in an organized manner. In the same way, interaction between the various cell organelles can only take place effectively over relatively short distances. The surface area of a cell is also an important factor influencing cell size. A large surface area is necessary for diffusion of substances into and out of the cell. As a cell enlarges the ratio of its surface area to volume decreases, and so cells of more than 100μ are seldom found. Furthermore, if specialization is to take place this is an easy way to carry it out. It is simplest to start with undifferentiated building units and gradually develop it into a specialized tissue.

Cell differentiation

Farther from the apex the cells divide less and less, usually becoming more elongated and vacuolated, gradually taking on the structure and functions of the specialized cells of the more mature plant. This differentiation has always posed something of a problem to the physiologist, as it is not known how cells placed together at the apex, and usually genetically identical, are capable of developing to form totally different types of specialized cells.

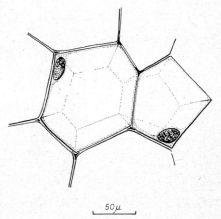

It is a mistake to take any type of cell as being 'typical'; while most meristematic cells look similar to one another, they are totally different from parenchymatous, palisade and other well-differentiated types. Parenchymatous cells are

FIG. 1.3. Parenchymatous cells from the stem cortex of the broad bean; cutaway view.

specialized as packing-cells; in the mass they form the tissue *parenchyma*. They are of complex shapes and many have six-sided faces, some eight-, five-, or four-sided faces. As these cells are tightly pressed together there are relatively few spaces between them and they are described as space-filling. The regular geometric shape that approaches nearest the typical parenchymatous cell is the tetrakaidecahedron (see figs. 1.3 and 1.4).

The palisade cell (see fig. 1.5), on the other hand, is specialized for photosynthesis and has a far greater content of chloroplasts than most

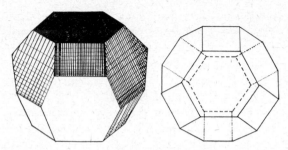

FIG. 1.4. The tetrakaidecahedron.

The space-filling geometric shape that resembles most closely the typical parenchymatous cell.

other cells in the stem and leaves. As is shown by the dense arrangement of these cells underneath the transparent epidermis, they are well adapted for this essential function.

Some of the most differentiated cells are in the conducting system. For

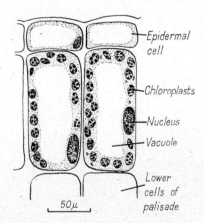

FIG. 1.5. Palisade cells of the privet leaf.

instance, the phloem sieve tubes, which are long and narrow, are lined with protoplasm and contain no nucleus. Each is joined to the next sieve tube through the multi-perforated sieve-plate, forming a highly evolved transport pathway for organic materials (see fig. 1.6). The water conducting

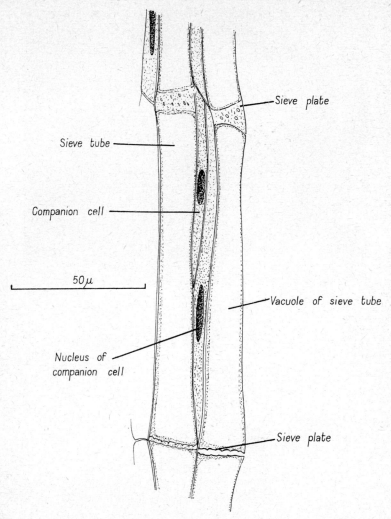

FIG. 1.6. Phloem cells of the artichoke stem.

elements of the system, the xylem, are even longer than the phloem elements. Their walls are heavily thickened with the complex carbohydrate
derivative lignin and lack protoplasmic contents in the mature state.

This brief summary of some highly developed cells and the tissues they
form may serve to emphasize that while almost all cells have certain basic
features in common, yet, if a plant is to be successful, some degree of specialization of cells and thus of tissue formation is a necessity. It is the net effect
of all the cells together that enables a plant to survive and compete in any
habitat.

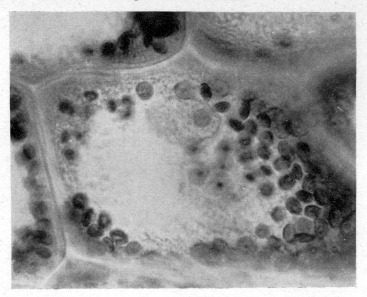

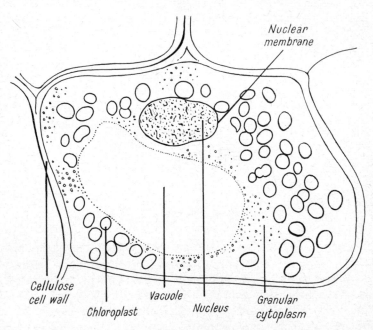

FIG. 1.7. A cell from the leaf of the Canadian pondweed (*Elodea canadensis*). (× 2000.)

2   Water Relations

2.1   Water and plant distribution

Water is such a familiar substance that we are liable to forget some of its important properties, without which life as we know it might well be impossible. Of these properties perhaps the most important relate to the maintenance of environmental stability. The high specific heat of water buffers sudden temperature changes and the expansion of water on freezing keeps lakes and rivers from freezing solid.

The requirement of the plant for water is widely recognized by farmer and horticulturalist as well as physiologist. In natural plant communities there are often clearly defined groups of plants, a particular group being adapted to a particular level of water availability. In temperate zones the class of plants that are most usual are referred to as *mesophytes* and these normally require water in the soil at most times of the year, while under conditions of more or less continuous water scarcity are found a group of specially adapted plants referred to as *xerophytes*. In both these groups the individual plant's water relations are of great importance. For instance, under natural conditions in a normal mesophyte community there are often zones of vegetation in which competition between one species and another must be very subtly controlled, and the ability of one species to survive is often related to water availability (though other factors, such as the mineral content and acidity of the soil, may also be important). In the plant communities of bogs, fens and by streams and ditches, there is often a clear zonation, one species being dominant over a small zone of particular soil water content, only to be replaced by another at a slightly different soil saturation level.

A typical fenland community in the Itchen Valley in Hampshire is shown in fig. 2.1. Here water availability rather than mineral content or soil acidity seems to be the most important factor controlling competition between the three strong-growing herbaceous species: nettle (*Urtica dioica*),

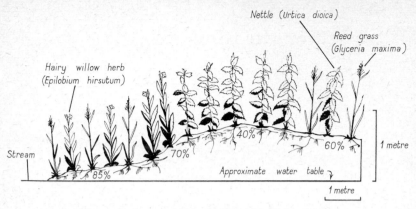

FIG. 2.1. An area of fenland in the Itchen Valley.
Percentages indicate water content of the topsoil. (Class result.)

hairy willow herb (*Epilobium hirsutum*) and reed grass (*Glyceria maxima*). Nettle is usually dominant at 40 per cent water content; reed grass at above 85 per cent (though it has a wide range of toleration); in between these figures there is competition between all three species, hairy willow herb probably succeeding best at about 70 per cent saturation. A similar example of the importance of water availability (but often coupled with other factors, such as soil acidity) occurs in bog communities. An example of part of a valley bog at Pendle Hill in Lancashire in an area of high rainfall and on a base-deficient soil is shown in fig. 2.2. Here the bog-moss

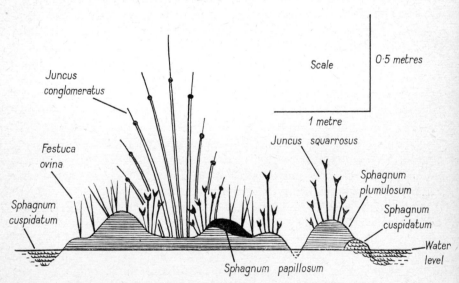

FIG. 2.2. A tussock in a valley bog, Pendle Hill, Lancashire.

(*Sphagnum cuspidatum*) occupies the wettest niche and is usually found growing in open water. As humus accumulates, tussocks are gradually formed above the water level; these become colonized by other *Sphagnum* species, such as *S. plumulosum*, which is able to tolerate much more drying out. The driest places near the tops of the tussocks are colonized by *S. papillosum* and *S. palustre*, as well as by rushes (*Juncus squarrosus* and *J. conglomeratus*) and also by sedges and grasses.

Clearly then, the different plants are differently adapted with respect to their water requirements, and water availability is an important feature of the environment. It is important to know how water is utilized within the plant, as those species which can utilize water more efficiently will often have a competitive advantage.

2.2 The need for water

One of the most important requirements for water within the plant is to keep the cell protoplasm in its correct physical state. If the protoplasm is to be properly organized and its enzymes, microscopic and sub-microscopic organelles correctly functioning, these minute, colloidal particles must be able to circulate freely in a watery matrix. Some substances such as proteins will be inactived or *denatured* unless properly *hydrated* by water molecules. Dissolved mineral materials must be available at areas of synthesis, and dissolved gases must be able to diffuse into and out of the cell; all this can happen only if the protoplasm is fully hydrated. In addition, water is also important in maintaining cell turgidity by the inflation of the water-containing vacuole. This is particularly important in many annual and perennial non-woody mesophytes, which have little cell lignification and are largely dependent on the turgidity of their cortical parenchyma for support. Lack of water in such a mesophyte is usually immediately obvious as wilting occurs. The large quantity of water in the plant means that it is often subject to *frost damage*. Freezing causes the water in the vacuole to swell and the cell may rupture. Many hardy plants are known to contain 'anti-freeze' substances in their vacuoles which prevent ice crystals from forming.

Another important need for water is to make up for loss caused by transpiration from the leaves and to a lesser extent from the stem. This loss is often considerable, and in large mesophytic trees is reported to be as much as several hundred gallons on a hot day, while even in a semi-xerophytic palm tree, it may be a hundred gallons a day. Transpiration has a few positive uses. First, it will cause a slight lowering of temperature in the leaf due to the absorption of the latent heat of vaporization of water, but this may only result in a cooling of a few degrees. The flow of water from root to stem which is necessitated by transpiration is a more important effect and is referred to as the transpiration stream. This is the chief means by which dissolved mineral salts are transported upwards in the xylem vessels or tracheids from root to leaf.

Finally, least in magnitude but of great importance, water is required to provide the hydrogen necessary for the synthesis of organic molecules. Photosynthesis is the process in which water is broken down to yield this hydrogen, which is then synthesised into carbohydrates by combination with carbon dioxide. A number of important reactions also involve the addition or removal of water.

2.3   Nature of the root system

If plants are to take up the water that they require they must, of course, have an efficient root system, well adapted to the ecological niche that

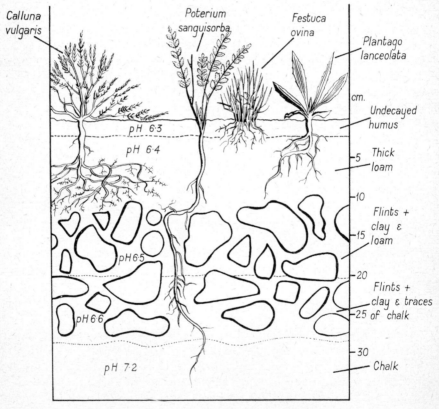

FIG. 2.3. Root systems of chalk heathland plants.

the plant normally occupies. One of the most variable features in the structure of vascular plants is the root; even in one area there is a great deal of variation from one plant species to another, and also to some extent among plants of the same species. This is shown in the vertical transect through an area of chalk heathland (see fig. 2.3). Some plants, such as salad burnet (*Poterium sanguisorba*), have a distinct tap-root going down several inches into the soil. Others, such as ling (*Calluna vulgaris*) and the grasses have a fibrous rooting system, making the most of the water contained in the rich humus-containing layer nearer the surface.

The actual area of water absorption is quite near the apex of the young growing root. There is very little cutinization or thickening near the apex,

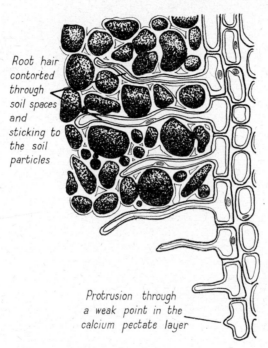

Root hair contorted through soil spaces and sticking to the soil particles

Protrusion through a weak point in the calcium pectate layer

FIG. 2.4. Root hairs and their development.

and water is able to diffuse easily into the internal spaces between the cortical cells. Most of the cells in this area are capable of taking up water, and so the total surface for water absorption is considerable. A large amount of water is also taken up through the root hairs, whose other main function is anchorage. The main hairs develop in the outermost layers of cells, usually about 2 or 3 mm. behind the root apex. Root-hair formation starts by a protrusion beginning to break through a weak point in the calcium pectate layer† of the cell surface (fig. 2.4). The root hair elongates gradually, cellulose being continuously added at the tip and the harder calcium pectate at the sides. Eventually the mature root hair is formed as a

† See page 130.

much convoluted thread, 3 or 4 mm. long, winding through the spaces between the soil particles and anchoring the root firmly in the soil. As the whole root grows in length and thickness, there is usually a considerable friction between the root hairs and the soil, so that the life of a root hair is not very prolonged and their zone often ends after 5 or 6 mm. Plants grown in soil-less culture produce roots with much larger root-hair systems because of the lack of abrasion.

2.4   Means of water uptake

The actual mechanism of water uptake is mostly due to the physical effect of osmosis. Osmosis is the process by which water or solvent passes through a semi-permeable membrane to dilute a stronger solution. In the cells of the root tip and in living plant cells generally the cell wall is a fully permeable membrane, the cytoplasm semi-permeable and the vacuole contains a fair concentration of dissolved material. That the cytoplasm is the membrane can be shown by placing tissues such as the staminal hairs of *Tradescantia virginiana* (which contain a deep red-purple anthocyanin pigment in their cell vacuoles) in a strong external solution (e.g. molar potassium nitrate) so as to cause *plasmolysis* (see fig. 2.5). As the vacuole shrinks due to water passing out into the stronger external solution the cytoplasm comes away from the cell wall, but the cell wall itself is not particularly distorted, indicating that it is freely permeable.

Osmosis is the chief means by which water is taken up into the root, and it is identical in principle to the physical demonstration of osmosis using the osmometer, in which the semi-permeable membrane is represented by a piece of bladder and the strong internal solution by potassium nitrate, copper sulphate or sugar solution. The pressure set up in the osmometer tube, or the force that has to be exerted to prevent osmosis taking place, is called the osmotic pressure.

It is also possible that in some cases there operates a non-osmotic system of water uptake, called *active uptake*, in which water is moved into the root and possibly from cell to cell by energy requiring processes connected with respiration, but little is known about the mechanism of such a process.

In a plant cell there are two factors determining whether a plant takes up or loses water. First there are the dissolved substances in the vacuole which determine the osmotic pressure or, more correctly, the *osmotic potential* of the cell sap. Second there is the elastic cell wall which exerts a force, the *wall pressure*, on the cell contents.

A plant is spoken of as being fully turgid when its cells are fully distended and no more water is taken up. At this point wall pressure equals the osmotic potential of the cell sap. At full turgor the force distending the cell wall, or *turgor pressure*, is equal and opposite to the wall pressure, and

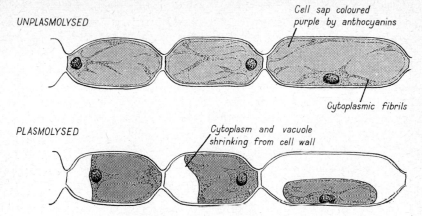

FIG. 2.5. Plasmolysis of *Tradescantia* staminal hairs.
A normal hair and the same after 1 hour in molar potassium nitrate.

therefore the same as the osmotic potential of the cell sap (fig. 2.6). If the cell is incompletely turgid more water may be taken up. This uptake of water depends on the difference between the osmotic potential and wall pressure. Formerly this was called the *suction pressure*, but this term is considered undesirable and the term *water diffusion potential* or simply *water potential* is now used instead. The water potential falls off as the cell becomes more turgid and the wall pressure increases. During this take-up the cell sap becomes progressively diluted, and consequently the osmotic potential also falls off. Measurements of the osmotic potential of the cell sap are usually

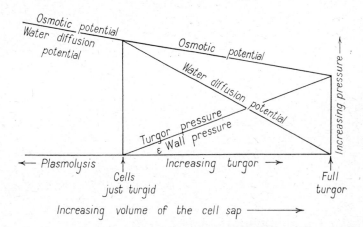

FIG. 2.6. Osmotic potential and the cell.
Changes in osmotic potential, water diffusion potential, turgor pressure and wall pressure, as conditions vary from plasmolysis to full turgor.

taken at incipient plasmolysis, that is when plasmolysis is just visible in about half the cells of the tissue being examined (see Appendix, p. 154). At this point water potential is the same as the osmotic potential, the wall pressure being nil. Other methods for measurement of the water potential of the cell sap make use of changes in weight or size of tissues when placed in solutions of different strengths (see Appendix, p. 155). There will be no change in size or weight of a tissue or cell when it is placed in a solution which is isotonic, or of the same water potential as the tissue. Typical results are shown in fig. 2.7. For the corona of a daffodil flower

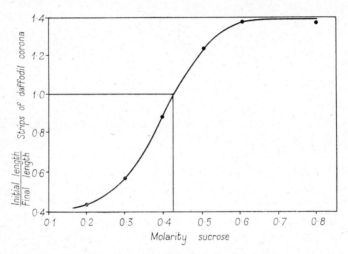

FIG. 2.7. Relationship between the concentration of the external solution and tissue size.

Where the initial/final length of the strip equals unity, the molarity of the sucrose is equivalent to the water potential. In this case the molarity is 0·42. At 20° C. this represents a water potential of 11·7 atmospheres (see Appendix, p. 155).

(Class result.)

the isotonic solution was 0·42M sucrose. For the accurate calculation of the water potential a knowledge of the temperature and the degree of ionization of the particular external solution at the particular temperature is necessary. Using unionized substances, such as sucrose at 0° C., the pressure exerted by molar solution is 22·4 atmospheres. The water potential of a 0·42M solution of sucrose is 11·7 atmospheres at 20° C.

2.5 Permeability of the cytoplasm

The phenomenon of plasmolysis indicates the importance of the cytoplasm as the semi-permeable membrane; some idea of its physical nature can be obtained from experiments relating the effects of external conditions to its permeability. One of the most important effects is that of temperature. As might be expected, knowing the cytoplasm to be a highly organized system of colloidal proteins, high temperature has the effect of destroying the semi-permeable nature of the cytoplasmic membrane. This is well shown by an experiment making use of the red anthocyanin pigment in the cell-sap of beetroot (see Appendix, p. 155). If similar-sized pieces of beetroot are immersed in water at a set temperature for one minute and then placed in distilled water for half an hour, the water is left coloured by the anthocyanins which have diffused out through the cytoplasm. Temperatures near boiling cause a deep red colour to be released, but at 60° C. the amount of red colour diffusing out falls off almost completely. This is the maximum temperature at which the cytoplasm can be maintained in its properly organized physical state, capable of acting as a semi-permeable membrane. This temperature is close to that which causes the coagulation of proteins and the breakdown of their colloidal state. Other more drastic treatments, for instance the use of a dehydrating agent such as alcohol, also cause the cytoplasm to become fully permeable. These experiments do not tell us what part of the cytoplasm is the actual semi-permeable membrane. Although experimental evidence is lacking, it could be one of three possibilities: first, the outer cytoplasmic membrane, the *plasma membrane*; secondly, the whole cytoplasm itself, and finally, the *tonoplast* or inner cytoplasmic membrane.

In addition to the various functions of the cytoplasm in metabolism, that of acting in part or whole as a semi-permeable membrane, and thus allowing the physical process of osmosis to take place, must rank as vitally important to the plant.

2.6 Water loss

Environmental factors affecting the rate of transpiration

There are two main techniques for investigating the rate of transpiration. The simpler methods involve weighing a whole plant, cut shoot or leaf. This will give the water loss in a given time. Alternatively, a potometer (fig. 2.8) may be used. This is an apparatus designed to estimate the rate of water uptake of an intact plant, or as is more usual, of a cut shoot, by observing the flow of water along a capillary tube to which the shoot is attached. Careful use of the potometer indicates the importance of the environmental conditions in determining the rate of transpiration or water loss. At the same time the rate of evaporation can be measured by use of the atmometer, a similar apparatus, but using a porous pot as the evaporating surface. It would be expected that the water loss from the plant would be on a parallel with the rate of evaporation and, provided that the other environmental conditions are constant, this is usually so. The rate of transpiration varies very much in the same way as the external physical conditions of temperature, atmospheric humidity and wind velocity affect the rate of evaporation from the purely physical system. If the effect of light is examined it is found that the rates of evaporation and transpiration are quite differently affected. Light itself has little effect on the rate of evaporation, but

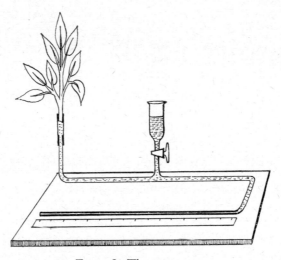

FIG. 2.8. The potometer.
An apparatus used to measure the rate of water uptake by a transpiring shoot.

in most mesophytes the rate of transpiration is much less in the dark than the light. This is well illustrated by the diurnal fluctuations in transpiration rate shown by hairy willow herb (*Epilobium hirsutum*) (see fig. 2.9. and also Appendix, p. 156, for a full description of the methods used). It is, of course, the effect of light in causing the opening and closing of the stomata that is the basis of this diurnal fluctuation.

Structural features of the plant which may affect the transpiration rate

Before looking at the mechanism which controls the opening and closing of the stomata it is worthwhile discussing the various anatomical features of the plant which may also affect the amount of water lost. The leaf structure varies to a remarkable extent, but probably the most important feature influencing the amount of water lost is the actual area of the leaves; plants living in humid areas lose water less readily by transpiration and are usually found with their leaves large and expanded. Many deciduous trees, particularly the tropical hardwoods, fall into this class, some of these have enormous pinnate leaves over 45 cm. long.

Many plants with considerable leaf areas have important adaptations which cut down excessive water loss. One interesting means is shown by the Himalayan shamrock pea (*Parochetus communis*), which orientates its leaf's edge on to the sun's rays so that there is a minimum heating effect. This adaptation is found in a number of plants, but more common adaptations which prevent excessive water loss concern the surface of the leaf itself. Cutin, a derivative of fatty acids, is almost impermeable to water vapour and, provided that the cuticular layer is sufficiently thick, loss of water

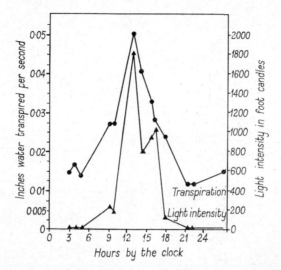

FIG. 2.9. Diurnal fluctuations in transpiration rate shown plotted with light intensity.

Data from estimation of the transpiration rate using the potometer and a cut piece of hairy willow herb (*Epilobium hirsutum*) of 390 sq. cm. leaf surface. Light intensity is measured by a photo-voltaic cell; temperature and evaporation rate can be measured at the same time. (See Appendix, p. 156, for a full description of the methods used.)

through the cuticle is not thought to be particularly important. In most plants, though, the amount of cutin covering the lower surface of the leaf is considerably less than is found in the upper, and it is possible that here cuticular transpiration may be more important. Continuous accurate weighing of a single leaf over a period of time has indicated the magnitude of cuticular water loss. The transpiration rate may show a characteristic decline curve (fig. 2.10). This can often be divided into three phases; first (A) being the rate of transpiration with the stomata open; at (B) the stomata close, and the last part of the curve (C) gives the rate of water loss through the cuticle. Electron-microscope photographs of carbon replicas of leaf surfaces show a great variety of surface; fig. 2.11 shows the layered

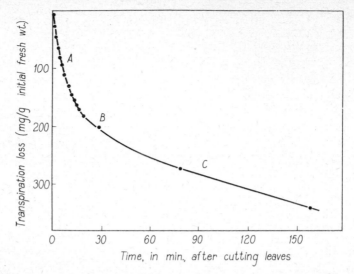

FIG. 2.10. Transpiration decline curve of ragwort (*Senecio Jacobaea*).
Leaves collected at 1055 a.m. (After Willis, A. J., and Jefferies, R. L. (1963).
'Investigations of the water relations of sand-dune plants.' *B.E.S. Symposium*.)

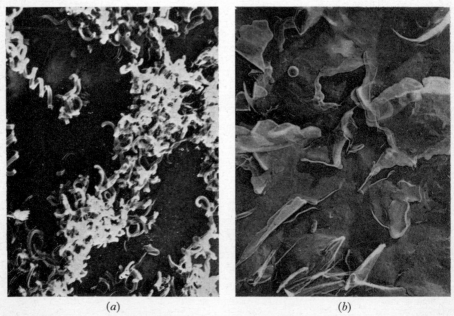

(a)   (b)

FIG. 2.11. The surface of leaves of (A) *Chrysanthemum segetum* and
(B) *Hyacinthus orientalis* (×12,000)

Carbon replica of the adaxial surface; electron microscope photograph. (Juniper
(1959). *Endeavour*, XVIII, No. 69, p. 20.)

protective system of waxy cutin covering found in the corn marigold (*Chrysanthemum segetum*) and hyacinth (*Hyacinthus orientalis*).

Hairiness of leaves is also frequently found in flowering plants, and is generally thought to help keep the leaf cool and also to prevent rapid wind currents from passing close to the surface of the leaf and thus removing water vapour from transpiring areas. Although hairiness is widespread in mesophytes, it is particularly frequent in plants growing at high altitudes, where high winds and high temperatures are frequently encountered. For instance, alpine mouse-ear chickweed (*Cerastium alpinum*), a local alpine plant found in the north of England and Scotland, is densely covered with long white hairs. In the Alps, typical high-altitude cushion plants, such as *Androsace imbricata*, are covered with a growth of short hairs, while *Eritrichium nanum* and edelweiss (*Leontopodium alpinum*) are densely pubescent.

As most mesophtyes have their stomata open in the light, allowing free gas transfer for photosynthesis and respiration, the stomatal distribution, shape and size are probably, second to the actual leaf area, the most important group of factors controlling water loss during the daytime. During the night the stomata are usually closed and cuticular transpiration may be relatively more important.

The distribution of stomata can be examined by making epidermal strips or by making a nail-varnish replica (see Appendix, p. 156). There is a surprisingly wide range of stomatal densities found in ordinary mesophytes; the garden iris has stomata on both sides of its leaves, with about 200 per sq. mm., the sunflower (*Helianthus annuus*) has about 330 per sq. mm. and the privet (*Ligustrum ovalifolium*) has 700 per sq. mm. Both the sunflower and the privet have their stomata confined to the lower surface of their leaves. These stomatal densities are considerably higher than those found in many xerophytes (p. 34).

The size and shape of the stomata are important anatomical features influencing the rate of transpiration. In most mesophytes the stomata are as shown in fig. 2.12, that is, they are nearly flush with the surface of the leaf; even so, the actual area of opening and closing, between the guard-cells, is very slightly sunk in many cases. (Extreme examples of the sunken stomata found in many xerophytes are discussed on page 34.) This small pocket of relatively still air may become highly saturated with water vapour, and this may result in an effective lowering in the rate of passage of water molecules from the saturated air spaces of the mesophyll out into the atmosphere. The size of the open pore itself is also important in determining the amount of water lost. It is subject to a good deal of variation from plant to plant, but typical dimensions, as in the garden rhododendron, are 0·006 mm. long and 0·001 mm. wide. However, Brown and Escombe found that a surface pierced by many small pores provides less resistance to the diffusion of water vapour than a similar surface pierced by a smaller number of larger holes of equivalent area. It is important, then, in comparing the stomatal organization of various plants, to consider the size of the pores in relation to their numbers and distribution.

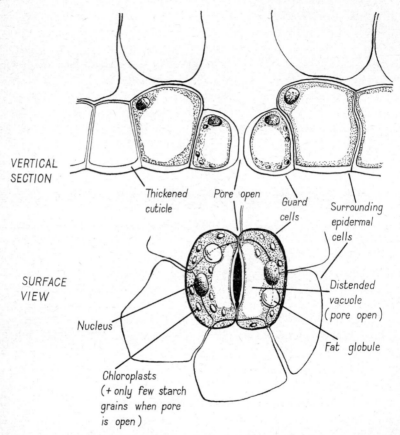

VERTICAL
SECTION

Thickened   Pore open   Guard   Surrounding
cuticle   cells   epidermal
                                          cells

SURFACE
VIEW   Distended
                                          vacuole
                                          (pore open)
Nucleus

Fat globule

Chloroplasts
(+ only few starch
grains when pore
is open)

FIG. 2.12. The stoma of the privet (*Ligustrum ovalifolium*) highly magnified.

The opening and closing of the stomata

A simple apparatus, called the porometer, can be used to measure the mass flow of gas through the leaf under different conditions. Early porometers such as that devised by Francis Darwin and Pertz in 1911 (see fig. 2.13) consisted of a cup sealed to the leaf surface (usually the lower surface). The time taken for the water in the vertical tube to fall gave a measurement of the rate of flow of gas through the leaf and indicated the resistance the leaf offered. A simple and efficient modern version is discussed in the Appendix on page 157. Using the porometer, the results illustrated in

fig. 2.14 were obtained. Here the surface of the leaf offers much less resistance to the loss of gas during the daytime than at night, which agrees well
with the visual evidence that the stomata are open in the light and closed
in the dark.

Stomata open when their guard cells are fully turgid and close when these
cells lose full turgidity. This effect can be shown by placing an epidermal

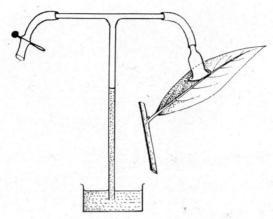

FIG. 2.13. Simple porometer of Darwin and Pertz. (After Maximov (1929).
The Plant in Relation to Water. Translated by R. H. Yapp. London, Allen
and Unwin.)

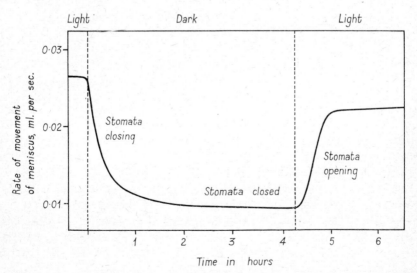

FIG. 2.14. The effect of illumination on the movement of the stomata of *Pelargonium*. (After Noel (1959). Some New Techniques in Plant Physiology,
School Science Review, No. 142, p. 497.)

strip of a plant such as the garden iris in a strong solution of potassium nitrate, so as to cause plasmolysis of the guard cells and closing of the stomata. It is, however, usually only under conditions of drought and wilting that the stomata close on account of the overall water level within the plant; under normal conditions it has been found that it is the amount of soluble carbohydrate in the guard cells which controls the opening and closing of the stomata.

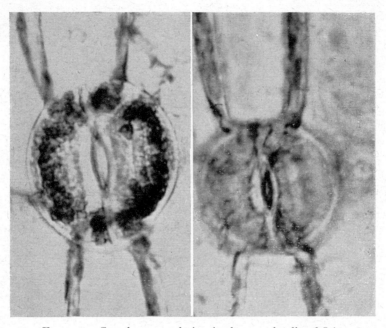

FIG. 2.15. Starch accumulation in the guard cells of *Iris*.
Left: strong accumulation after 24 hours in the dark; *right:* after 12 hours in the light. Stained in iodine. (Highly magnified.)

Under dark conditions, when no photosynthesis is taking place, starch tends to accumulate. Under light conditions the starch gradually disappears and sucrose appears instead in the vacuoles of the guard cells. The starch, which is in the cytoplasm, is relatively insoluble and osmotically inactive, and so the guard cells tend to lose turgor and close, while the sucrose, accumulating in the vacuole, increases its osmotic potential so that the guard cells take up more water and, in swelling, take up a shape which results in the opening of the stomatal pore (see figs. 2.15 and 2.16 on p. 27). There are several curious points about the stomatal mechanism. In the first place it is peculiar that the guard cells should accumulate starch in the dark, while the majority of plant cells form starch only in daylight. A second curious phenomenon is that in spite of light and dark treatments

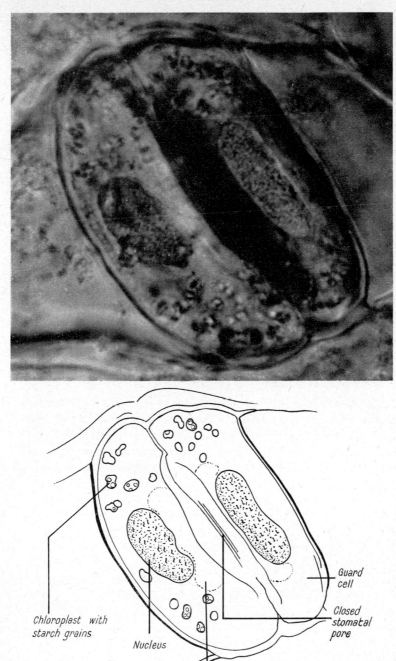

Fig. 2.16. The stoma of spiderwort (*Tradescantia virginiana*). (Highly magnified.)

C

that a leaf may receive, many plants seem to have an autonomic rhythm for
stomatal movements. For instance, if a particular plant normally has its
stomata open during the day and closed at night, then if it is given continuous daylight it may still keep to its normal time-table for several days!
We are therefore quite a way from understanding the full mechanism of
stomatal movement.

Water loss by guttation

When a plant is growing under conditions of high soil-water content
and high atmospheric humidity small droplets of water are often seen at
more or less regular intervals around the edge of the leaf. Such conditions
are often noticed in a greenhouse after copious watering the previous even-
ing followed by a relatively cool night. This exudation is called *guttation*
and normally occurs through specialized structures called hydathodes
which are found at the edges of the leaves close to the endings of the xylem
vessels. This type of water loss, unlike transpiration, is to a large extent
under metabolic control, and the process bears in this respect a simi-
larity to the phenomenon referred to as root pressure, in which considerable water pressures are developed in the roots. How important it is to the
plant it is difficult to say, but it seems likely that it allows for a continued
flow of water and dissolved materials through the plant even when transpiration is low.

2.7   Transport of water

A normally turgid leaf contains water in its vacuoles, cytoplasm, cell
walls and inter-cellular spaces. Transpiration results in the removal of
water, primarily from the last two of these areas; these are referred to as
the *outer-space* or *apoplast*. The lowering of *hydrostatic pressure* caused by
evaporation could result in water movement either from the vacuoles of
leaf cells or from the vascular system via further cell walls and inter-
cellular spaces. Recently Weatherley has shown that relatively little water
comes from the cell vacuoles and most of the movement is through the
apoplast system. Movement of water into and out of the cells does still
take place as alterations in their osmotic potentials occur; these can be
brought about by metabolic processes such as photosynthesis. It is thought
that such movement is small in magnitude compared with that occurring
through the apoplast system. Loss of water from the finest xylem elements
is made good by a corresponding uptake in the root. The xylem, in spite
of the extreme narrowness of its vessels (0·038 cm. diameter) and tracheids
(0·004 cm. diameter), acts as a long and continuous tube from root to leaf.
Tall columns of water have an extreme ability to stand up to tensions without breaking, and it is thought that the sun's energy, causing the evaporation from the leaf, is enough to account for most of the ascent of water in

both herbaceous plants and tall trees. That this transpiration pull or *shoot-tension* can exert a considerable force is well shown by the experiment in which a shoot of cedar is attached to a long glass tube filled with water and dipped into mercury. With an atmospheric pressure of 76 cm. of mercury, the mercury in the tube rose to over 101 cm., indicating a considerable force exerted by the plant (see fig. 2.17).

That most of the water is transported in the xylem rather than the phloem is also easily demonstrated by placing a cut shoot of a rapidly transpiring plant, such as the balsam or Busy-Lizzie (*Impatiens sultani*), in dilute aqueous eosin or methylene-blue dye. After a few hours sections cut high up the shoot will show that most of the dye is clearly in the xylem regions. This can be confirmed by another simple experiment, in which the cut end of a leafy shoot of a woody plant is prepared so that the xylem and phloem can be covered separately with wax. With the xylem blocked, upwards transport of water is prevented and the plant wilts, but a shoot with the phloem blocked is unaffected (see fig. 2.18).

The lowering in pressure at the bottom of the finest xylem vessels will allow water to pass into them from surrounding areas. Again, there are two possibilities; water could be drawn from the apoplast of the root system or from the vacuoles. The work of Weatherley has shown that in this area water movement is subject to conditions affecting the cytoplasm (e.g. temperature) and so it seems likely that at least part of the movement involves transport of water *through* living cells. The semi-continuous cytoplasmic system is referred to collectively as the *symplast*. The root endodermis with its lignified and suberized *Casparian strip* is one site

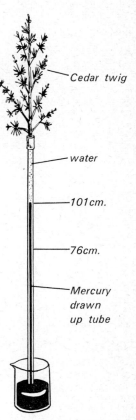

FIG. 2.17. Demonstration of shoot tension. (After Greulach (1957). 'The Rise of Water in Plants', *Plant Life*, New York: Scientific American.)

where water must move almost exclusively through the symplast. Much of the movement through the rest of the root could, however, still be through the apoplast. Apart from the endodermis, it is therefore possible to visualize a continuous apoplast from soil water surrounding the cells of the root apex, right through the plant to the surfaces of the leaf cells.

While the bulk of this water movement in plants is concerned in making good the transpiration loss, a certain amount of dissolved minerals, taken up from the soil by active, energy-requiring systems, is transported along in the main transpiration stream, and in this way are carried near to areas, such as the stem apex, where active metabolism is occurring.

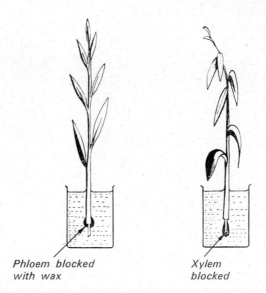

Phloem blocked   Xylem
with wax   blocked

FIG. 2.18. The path of movement of water in the stem. The effect of covering the xylem and phloem with wax.

2.8 Halophytes and xerophytes

Not all plants live in conditions where water is readily available through-out a great part of the year; such plants are particularly useful in studying water relations, as they may have interesting adaptations of considerable survival value in their special environments. There are essentially two classes of plants which can tolerate lack of available water. In the first case there are the *xerophytes* which are adapted to survive conditions of actual drought and water scarcity. In the second case there are those plants which may be living in conditions where there is plenty of water, but this contains so much dissolved material that normal mesophytes are unable to survive as their cells become plasmolysed. Plants living in salt marshes are called *halophytes*.

The halophytes

The most usual adaptation in halophytes is a physiological one. That is, their cells have a much higher osmotic potential than is found in mesophytes, and in this way the plants are able to obtain their water under most conditions. Fig. 2.19 shows a transect across part of a salt marsh near Keyhaven in Hampshire. Details of the osmotic potential of their leaves measured at incipient plasmolysis are also given.

Salt-marsh plants are adapted to their environment in several other ways. A common adaptation is that they often have a well-developed rhizome and rooting system which helps them to resist tidal action and bind the mud. Many of the grasses are specialized in this way; an outstanding example is the cord-grass, *Spartina townsendii*, which has colonised vast areas of mud-flat around the British Isles. Many of the smaller plants frequently have succulent leaves; in some cases, such as the scarlet pimpernel, *Anagallis*

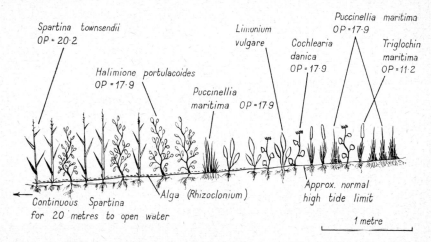

FIG. 2.19. Salt marsh plants and the osmotic potential of their cell sap, Key-haven, Hampshire. (Osmotic potentials are given in atmospheres.)

arvensis ssp. arvensis, the succulence may be only an environmental modi-fication which is lost when the plant is transferred to an area which does not contain salt in the soil. In other cases, such as the annual glassworts (*Salicornia* species), the plants are always succulent. Succulence is an important adaptation which helps the plants to survive in their unusual ecological niche. At some times of the day the plants may be bathed in sea-water of fairly low osmotic pressure, but at low tide considerable dry-ing out may occur, and this will result in the osmotic potential of the soil solution rising considerably. If the strength of the soil solution becomes higher than that in the plant, then 'physiological drought' will occur and the plant will be unable to take up more water, and water may even be withdrawn from the plant. Storage of water in succulent leaves may help the plant to tide over these difficult times of the day. Halophytes, then, are a group of plants which have several interesting adaptations to enable them to obtain the water that they require for life in what might appear to be a rather unfavourable environment.

The xerophytes

Xerophytes are plants which show a variety of adaptations enabling them to survive conditions of drought and water scarcity. They are found in a range of species from the true cacti of the *Cactaceae*, often plants of arid deserts, through the succulent species with swollen stems and leaves, to those plants which have no obvious external adaptations but which are nevertheless well adapted physiologically.

The xerophytes are best divided from the point of view of their various adaptations into two classes, the *drought evaders* and the *drought endurers*. The former class consists of those plants which really evade the issue and survive times of drought by existing as a seed or even as a spore. Much of the famous desert ephemeral vegetation is made up of annuals which come to flowering quickly in a wet period and then survive the ensuing dry one in the form of seeds. The Californian poppy (*Eschscholtzia californica*) is a well-known example of such a drought evader.

Truer xerophytic adaptations are found in those plants which are adapted to *endure* water loss. In several cases, such as the creosote bush (*Covillea glutinosa*), a North American desert plant, the plant looks superficially much like any mesophyte, but has a high tolerance of desiccation, the protoplasm being able to retain its organization when the whole plant is in a highly dehydrated state. Many members of the Bryophyta and Pteridophyta have a rather unexpected tolerance to desiccation of this sort. For instance many mosses live in particularly dry areas; *Tortula muralis* is a common moss growing on walls and on rocks in the British Isles, and although it may appear to be completely dried out, revives quickly after a shower of rain. There are also several examples of Pteridophytes that are similarly able to withstand desiccation; the American resurrection plant (*Selaginella lepidophylla*) is often sold as a curiosity, as it exists in a rolled-up state when dry and rapidly unrolls when moistened. The ability of plants to stand up to protoplasmic desiccation is very considerable and is probably also found in a great many xerophytes with other adaptations.

Another means for the endurance of water loss is to have a large water-storage system which enables the plant to survive the period of drought. This is found in many succulents which may have a high transpiration rate but which may still be able to survive in a desert region. In Britain many stonecrops (*Sedum* species) are in this class and are common plants of roofs, walls and rocks. Water is stored in large parenchymatous, frequently mucilage-containing cells of the leaf and stem. Endurance of water loss may also be possible if the plant has a sufficiently deep root system to enable it to obtain water throughout the period of drought. Such a system is particularly common in many Mediterranean trees and shrubs, such as the acacia and oleander.

The most interesting group of xerophytes is that group of drought endurers which is adapted to prevent water loss. There are a great many

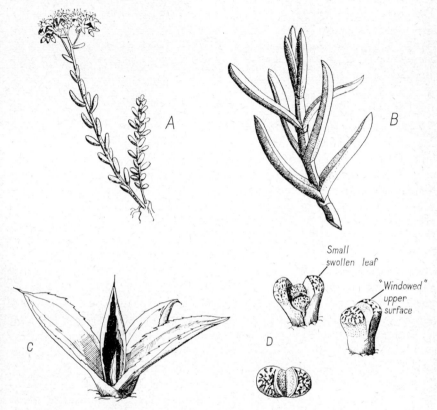

FIG. 2.20. A series of leaf succulents. ($\times \frac{1}{2}$.)
A. The white stonecrop (*Sedum album*). B. The Hottentot fig (*Carpobrotus edulis*).
C. The century plant (*Agave americana*).
D. A pebble plant (*Lithops helmuti*). An extreme form of leaf succulent. The chlorophyllous cells are deep down lining the leaf interior and the upper surface is nearly transparent. Many *Lithops* are nearly buried in pebbles but are still able to photosynthesize through this 'window' arrangement.

adaptations towards this end, but the simplest means of reducing water loss concerns reduction of the surface : volume ratio of the whole plant (and this at the same time usually results in succulence). Plants can normally be classified into stem and leaf succulents on this basis. The least well-adapted in the leaf-succulent series are possibly species of *Sedum* (see fig. 2.20). Here the leaves are swollen but there is little lowering of the area from which transpiration may occur. The Hottentot fig (*Carpobrotus edulis*) is better adapted. In this the opposite leaves are closely packed down on one another. Other well-adapted species take the form of a rosette; the magnificent species of *Agave* that are common on the hillsides of the south of France are good examples of this class. The best-adapted of the leaf-succulent series is the genus *Lithops*. These look like pebbles and are found embedded in the soil of the Kalahari desert in South Africa. In *Lithops helmuti* the leaves are very swollen and sunk deeply in the soil; the upper surface of the leaf is transparent (see fig. 2.20) and thus allows for more efficient photosynthesis by the cells lining the inside edges of the leaves. For this reason they are often called 'window-plants'.

In the stem-succulent series the simplest type of adaptation is seen in *Kleinia articulata*, the candle plant; this has well-developed, though slightly succulent leaves and a thick, succulent stem, the leaves being shed during periods of drought (see fig. 2.21). Leaf-shedding is a common feature of both mesophytes and xerophytes in times of extreme drought. The most famous example of stem succulents are in the cactus family itself; the best-adapted species are found in the genera *Carnegiea* and *Cereus*. In these the stem is a simple, grooved upright structure with only occasional branches, true leaves are absent, but their place is taken by spines which line the edges of the stem. In some stem-succulents the adaptations have, in a sense, gone too far and the stems have a flattened and almost leaf-like appearance; *Opuntia ficus-indica*, which forms a large bushy plant with rounded stem segments up to 40 cm. long, and the smaller *Epiphyllum* species fall into this class. The competitive ability of some of the prickly pears (*Opuntia inermis* in particular) is well known. These plants colonized vast areas of Australia—some 60 million acres—before they were brought under control by the larva of the moth *Cactoblastis cactorum*.

In addition to these gross adaptations which give the plant a small surface from which transpiration may take place, many xerophytes have other less conspicuous adaptations which cut down water loss. A thick, waxy cuticle, as is found in *Kleinia*, is useful in reducing cuticular transpiration, while loss through the stomata is cut down primarily through their density being much less than is found in ordinary mesophytes (p. 23). For instance, *Opuntia ficus-indica* has about 100 per sq. mm., while *Cereus chende* has only about 30 per sq. mm. Loss through the stomata is also reduced by their arrangement in pits, sometimes surrounded by a system of hairs. This is well illustrated by the marram grass (*Ammophila arenaria*), which rolls its leaf up under dry conditions so that water molecules, diffusing out of the stomata, follow an indirect route.

Many xerophytes, particularly succulents allied to *Mesembryanthemum*, possess an interesting physiological condition in that they have an inverted stomatal rhythm, their stomata being closed during the day and

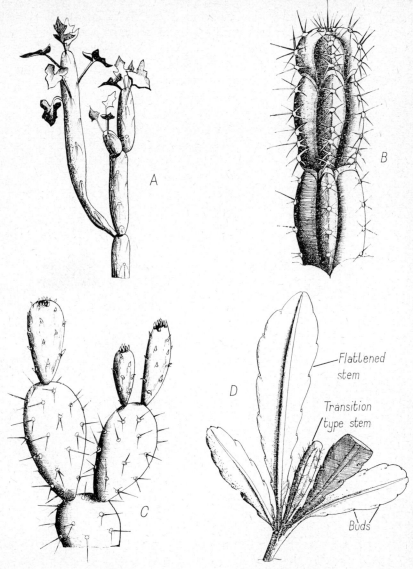

FIG. 2.21. A series of stem succulents. (× ⅓.)

A. The candle plant (*Kleinia articulata*). The leaves are shed in times of drought. Water is stored in the swollen stem.

B. *Cereus peruvianus*. No true leaves are found, but their position is taken by spines.

C. Prickly pear (*Opuntia ficus-indica*). The oval, flattened stem segments are almost leaf-like in appearance.

D. Orchid cactus (*Epiphyllum crenatum*). An extreme example of a stem-succulent in which many of the stem segments are most leaf-like in appearance.

open at night. This adaptation may be of particular importance as a method for water conservation, provided that sufficient carbon dioxide assimilation is possible during daylight, when photosynthesis is taking place.

Xerophytes and halophytes have a series of adaptations which appear to be useful in their particular environments. In temperate-region plant communities water is still one of the most important factors, and the distribution of many species is closely correlated with water availability, though it is usually much more difficult to find what features mesophytes possess which enable them to compete successfully for water.

3   Photosynthesis

3.1   Introduction

Although water availability is one of the most obvious factors influencing plant distribution, light is probably just as important an ecological factor.

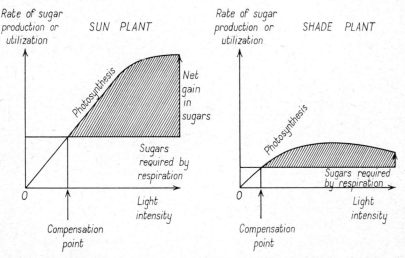

FIG. 3.1. The photosynthetic efficiency of sun and shade plants. (After Ashby: *Introduction to Plant Ecology*. London, Macmillan & Co.)

Both light intensity and quality affect the rate at which plants can manufacture the complex organic materials that they require for their stores of energy. In woodland communities, for instance, plants are differently adapted, particularly to light intensity. The dominant tree species are usually sun plants, thriving in high light intensities, but having seedlings

37

which are usually capable, as in the oak, of tolerating shade conditions. The plants of herb and shrub layers differ markedly from one another in their light requirements, though many of them complete the main part of their life cycle in the spring before shading from the leaf canopy takes place. Respiration goes on all the time. When the light intensity is sufficient to allow photosynthesis to take place so that the rates of the two pro-

Position on beech tree	Height from ground	Plant found	Minimum light intensity required to complete the compensation period in 2 hr. (*lux*)	Optimum intensity required to complete the compensation period (*lux*)	Ecological class of plants
Stump	30–60 cm.	Bryophytes, e.g. *Thuidium*, *Hylocomium*, *Thamnium*	400	10,000	Shade plants
Trunk	480–510 cm.	Bryophytes, e.g. *Anomodon* and some lichens	1,200	15,000	Intermediate group between shade and sun
Crown	795–810 cm.	Mostly lichens, e.g. *Parmelia* and the bryophyte *Ulota crispula*	6,000 2,000	20,000 20,000	Sun plants

Modified *after* Hosokawa and Odani (1957.) Compensation period and vertical range of Epiphytes. *Journal of Ecology*, **45**, No. 3, p. 901.

cesses are the same, then the plant is said to be at its *compensation point*. At this point there is no net gain or loss of either carbon dioxide or oxygen. Shade plants can utilize low light intensities more efficiently than sun plants and so attain their compensation point earlier in the day (see fig. 3.1). Similarly, they are able to make up quicker for the loss of carbohydrate that has occurred due to respiration during the dark. The time taken is called the *compensation period*. A plant that is slow in completing its compensation period will tend to be at a disadvantage compared with a faster neighbour, as new synthesis and growth may be delayed and the plant out-grown and out-competed. On the other hand, these shade plants which have a short compensation period are unable to utilize the high light intensities so efficiently. Measurements of the compensation period of bryophytes growing on tree-trunks and branches have shown that light is an important factor in affecting the competition between species of rather similar habit growing on much the same substrate. Results of work on epiphytes growing on beech trees in Japan are given in the table on page 38. A method used in determining the compensation period is given in the Appendix on p. 159.

Although some plants may have slight anatomical differences when growing in the shade, for instance the number of palisade layers is often reduced, nevertheless, the mechanisms are largely unknown by which different plants are able to photosynthesize more effectively than others and obtain a competitive advantage. The answer to this problem may well lie in the mechanism of the process of photosynthesis itself.

Photosynthesis is not the only process by which living things are able to synthesize carbohydrates. For instance, many bacteria are able to live by chemosynthetic means. They obtain the energy they require by means of inorganic changes, that is, from reactions of an inorganic oxidation–reduction type, instead of using sunlight as their energy source. But photosynthesis, being the main process by which the basic food of the plants and animals is produced, must still have a vital position in the biological world.

3.2 An outline of the process

Essentially the process involves the combination or fixation of carbon dioxide; hydrogen, released from water, is then used to reduce the combined carbon dioxide so as to form a carbohydrate. Sunlight is necessary to provide the energy for the splitting of water into hydrogen and oxygen. This reaction takes place only in the presence of the green substance, chlorophyll, which acts as a catalyst, converting light energy into chemical energy. The following two equations can be used to summarize these steps:

(i)
$$2H_2O \xrightarrow[\text{chlorophyll}]{\text{light}} 4H + O_2$$

(ii)
$$CO_2 + 4H \longrightarrow (CH_2O) + H_2O$$

In the second equation (CH_2O) is used to represent a simple carbohydrate. If these two equations are added together a single general equation is obtained:

(iii)
$$H_2O + CO_2 \longrightarrow (CH_2O) + O_2$$

In fact no such simple carbohydrate exists, but hexose sugars ($C_6H_{12}O_6$) and starch are frequently found and so the following general equation is still often used:

$$\text{(iv)} \qquad 6CO_2 + 6H_2O \xrightarrow[\text{chlorophyll}]{\text{light}} C_6H_{12}O_6 \quad + 6O_2$$

hexose sugar   starch

A series of quite simple tests can be used to verify this equation.

(1) *Necessity for carbon dioxide*

Cover a few leaves of dead-nettle or an ovate-leaved plant for about ten hours so that any starch already in the leaves due to previous photosynthesis may be removed. Fill two large specimen tubes, one with 2 ml. strong potassium hydroxide to remove any carbon dioxide, and the other with 2 ml. distilled water, or a saturated solution of sodium chloride, as a control. Place one leaf in each tube, so that half the leaf-blade is inside the tube and half outside; carefully cork the tubes (see fig. 3.2). If possible keep the leaves attached to the plant throughout the experiment, otherwise place the tubes in a sealed jar containing a little water; this prevents the leaf from wilting. Illuminate them brightly, preferably with a fluorescent light system, for about two hours, then remove the leaves. Mark with a nick the one that has been in the carbon dioxide-free atmosphere and kill the leaves by immersing them for a few seconds in boiling water. Finally, extract the chlorophyll from the leaf by boiling it for a few minutes in 90 per cent ethanol on a water-bath. Test each leaf for starch with iodine solution; there should

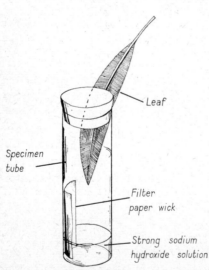

Leaf

Specimen tube

Filter paper wick

Strong sodium hydroxide solution

Fig. 3.2. Device used to show that carbon dioxide is necessary for photosynthesis.

be no starch in the part of the leaf that has been in the carbon dioxide-free atmosphere, but both the water control and also the part of the leaf that has been outside the specimen tube should possess starch.

(2) *Necessity for water*

For photosynthesis to take place the plant must be fully hydrated and its cells turgid. There are no simple tests to show how water is utilized.

(3) *Necessity for light*

Keep a *Pelargonium* plant in the dark for about ten hours to remove any starch. Cover part of the leaf with black paper to exclude light and illuminate brightly for about two hours, remove the chlorophyll and test for starch

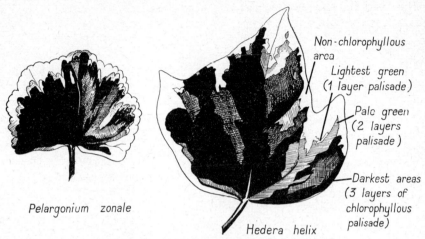

Pelargonium zonale

Hedera helix

Non-chlorophyllous area
Lightest green (1 layer palisade)
Pale green (2 layers palisade)
Darkest areas (3 layers of chlorophyllous palisade)

FIG. 3.3. Variegated leaves of garden geranium (*Pelargonium zonale*) and ivy (*Hedera helix*).

as described in (1) above. Starch should be present only in that part of the leaf that has been exposed to light.

(4) *Necessity for Chlorophyll*

After a period of bright sunlight pick a few young leaves of a variegated plant such as *Acer negundo variegatum*, *Elaeagnus pungens aureovariegata* or a variegated form of *Pelargonium* (see fig. 3.3.). Trace the pattern of the variegation, extract the chlorophyll and test for starch in the usual way. Starch should be present only in those parts of the leaf that originally contained chlorophyll.

(5) *The formation of carbohydrates*

The presence of free hexose sugars (e.g. glucose) in leaves that have been photosynthesizing can be shown by Benedict's test (see p. 158). Make a cell extract by grinding in a mortar a few leaves of *Tropaeolum*, *Pelargonium* or onion. Remove most of the chloroplast and cell-wall material by filtering or centrifuging and test the clear liquid for soluble reducing sugar. Quantitative treatment may allow for comparison of the amounts of reducing sugar formed in different plants under a variety of circumstances. The density of the red copper oxide precipitate is a measure of the amount of sugar present.

Although hexose sugars are regarded as the primary product of photosynthesis, they are normally converted to starch rather quickly. As starch is a relatively insoluble carbohydrate, it tends to remain where it is formed, and thus, in many ways it is easier to test for the presence of starch rather than hexose sugars when endeavouring to demonstrate the occurrence of photosynthesis.

(6) *Production of Oxygen*

Keep some fresh sprigs of *Elodea canadensis* under water, with a funnel and test-tube set up to collect any gases evolved. Place in a well-lighted place, and after a reasonable quantity of gas has been collected, test for the presence of oxygen either with a glowing splint or, better, with alkaline pyrogallol (see Appendix, pages 161 and 205).

These experiments are useful in that they illustrate the overall equation, but it has been realized for many years that photosynthesis is a much more complex and many stage process.

3.3   Evidence that photosynthesis is a several stage process

In the 1920s F. F. Blackman investigated the effects of light intensity and temperature on the rate of photosynthesis. He worked with the aquatic willow moss (*Fontinalis antipyretica*), which is particularly useful for such experiments, as the plant possesses no stomata or cuticular thickening, and takes up carbon dioxide readily from its aquatic medium. Similar experiments can be carried out using the aquatic *Elodea canadensis*. Well-illuminated pieces of *Elodea* produce bubbles of a gas, which is mostly oxygen, from their leaves and cut ends of stems (see Appendix, p. 160). The number of bubbles produced from a single stem in a given time gives an indication of the rate of photosynthesis. By varying the distance of the light from the stem it is possible to work out the relationship between light intensity and the rate of the process (see fig. 3.4). The rate of photosynthesis is seen to be directly related to light intensity up to a point; then some other factor, possibly carbon dioxide availability, affects or *limits* the rate of photosynthesis.

A similar experiment can be carried out to determine the effect of temperature. If this is operated at low light intensity, a rise in temperature from 18° to 28° C. makes little difference to the rate of the reaction, but if it is carried out at a high light intensity the rate of photosynthesis is doubled. In the first case light intensity is limiting the rate of the reaction. The second experiment shows that there must be a distinct chemical, non-light requiring stage or stages in photosynthesis as well as a purely photochemical one. Ordinary chemical reactions are strongly influenced by temperature, and for a 10° rise in temperature, normally show a doubling in rate. They are then said to have a Q_{10} of two. Light-controlled re-

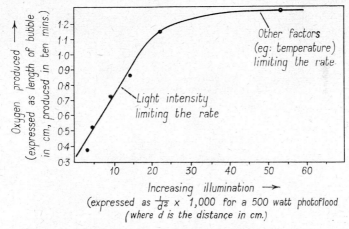

FIG. 3.4. The relationship between light intensity and rate of photosynthesis. (Class result.)

actions are temperature insensitive and show no change in rate over the same range in temperature, hence their $Q_{10} = 1$.

These experiments suggest then the existence of three stages in photosynthesis. First, a *diffusion stage*, in which the rate of the process may be governed by the availability of carbon dioxide and the rate with which it can diffuse into the photosynthesizing cell; secondly, a *light-requiring stage*; and thirdly, one or more *chemical stages*. The existence of a fourth stage, the *combination stage*, in which carbon dioxide is accepted, or fixed, even in the dark, is shown by keeping a plant in the dark in an atmosphere containing carbon dioxide isotopically labelled with C^{14}. Autoradiographs produced by placing a photographic plate over the leaves of the plant should show some accumulation of the tracer in the leaves, though there will be less than in those parts exposed to the light (see fig. 3.5 and Appendix, p. 172).

3.4 Detailed examination of the stages of photosynthesis: The diffusion stage

The main factors controlling the diffusion of gases into and out of the leaf are the structure of the leaf itself and also the physical conditions: temperature, humidity, wind velocity and light intensity, which may have

D

direct or indirect effects. A certain amount of carbon dioxide undoubtedly enters the leaf through the upper and lower epidermis, as normal mesophytes have only a fairly thin cuticle overlying the epidermal layers. There

Fig. 3.5. Autoradiograph of a shoot of tomato that has been in an atmosphere containing $C^{14}O_2$ for 12 hours. Note that a small amount of tracer is present in areas that have been shielded from the light. (Marked with an ✻.)

is little doubt though that the stomata are normally the chief means by which gaseous exchange takes place. (See discussion of stomata on p. 23.)

Further information about the diffusion stage can be obtained by treating a leaf so as to prevent gases from entering it. In the following experiment the amount of diffusion through the upper and lower surfaces can be compared.

To investigate the means of entry of carbon dioxide into the leaf

Keep a plant of *Pelargonium* in the dark for twenty-four hours to remove any starch. Then treat as follows four young leaves intact on the plant:

(1) Vaseline both surfaces.
(2) Vaseline the under surface only.
(3) Vaseline the upper surface only.
(4) Leave untreated.

Take care not to damage the leaves when applying the vaseline. Illuminate the leaves with bright fluorescent lamps. After some hours kill the leaves by dipping them in boiling water, extract the chlorophyll in 90 per cent ethanol, boiling on a water-bath, and test for starch with iodine.

As would be expected, most starch accumulates in the untreated leaf and in that which was vaselined only on the upper surface. This experiment emphasizes the importance of the diffusion stage and the structure of the leaf itself in determining the amount of gaseous diffusion, and thus the amount of photosynthesis.

3.5 The combination stage

After carbon dioxide has diffused into the air spaces between the cells of the mesophyll of the leaf it combines with water to form carbonic acid. This is the first step in the combination stage; transport of carbon dioxide in the form of carbonic acid takes place from the mesophyll to the palisade cells until the main site of photosynthesis is reached. The reaction with water is easily reversed, but use of radioactive labelled carbon dioxide, $C^{14}O_2$, indicates that even in the dark there is an accumulation of carbon dioxide which does not escape. In other words, the carbon dioxide has somehow become irreversibly fixed into the mesophyll and palisade cells.

A full explanation of the mechanism of fixation has come largely from the use of C^{14} in conjunction with paper chromatography. Paper chromatography provides us with a method for identifying any intermediates and products of a reaction, while use of tracer carbon can indicate the reaction pathway.

Use of labelled carbon dioxide and paper chromatography in working out the details of the combination stage

The usual materials used in experiments of this kind are unicellular green algae such as *Chlorella* or *Scenedesmus*. These are placed in a large flat-sided flask which can be brightly illuminated and which can be connected to a supply of labelled carbon dioxide. Sampling is carried out by opening the tap on the funnel and allowing some of the algae and their watery medium to pass into a tube containing methanol. This immediately kills them, and an extract of the materials formed in the algae is easily obtained from the alcohol. The apparatus used is illustrated in fig. 3.6. The extract is then examined by the paper chromatographic technique (see Appendix, p. 162).

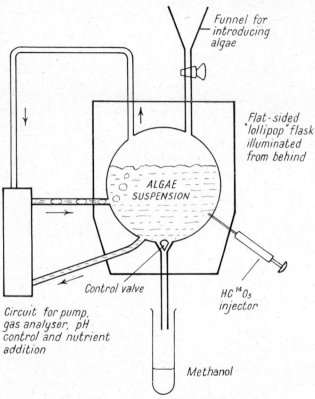

Funnel for
introducing
algae

Flat-sided
"lollipop" flask
illuminated
from behind

ALGAE
SUSPENSION

Control valve

Circuit for pump,
gas analyser, pH
control and nutrient
addition

$HC^{14}O_3$
injector

Methanol

FIG. 3.6. Apparatus used for obtaining extracts of algae that have been photosynthesizing in $C^{14}O_2$. (After Bassham (1962). The Path of Carbon in Photosynthesis. *Scientific American*, **206**, No. 6, p. 88.)

Tracer appearance on the chromatogram is quite easily analysed by placing the tube of a Geiger counter over the various spots on the chromatogram and recording the number of ionizations per second in each case. Alternatively, the chromatogram can be placed on a sheet of photographic negative for a few days. The negative will be exposed where tracer is present in the spot. A version of this technique is described in the Appendix on p. 174.

Results using tracer and chromatography on the dark-fixation or combination
  stage

If the algae which have been in the dark for some hours and in an atmosphere of $C^{14}O_2$ are analysed as described above, it is found that there is little accumulation of tracer in the leaf. If, however, analysis of the algae is done after a preceding light period, applying the $C^{14}O_2$ at the moment the light is switched off, then labelled phosphoglyceric acid (PGA) appears on the chromatogram.† This acid is formed as a product of carbon dioxide fixation in photosynthesis. Obviously the carbon dioxide must combine with something to form PGA ($CH_2O\,\widehat{P}.CHOH.COOH$); it is possible that some carbon dioxide acceptor is formed in the light period which is

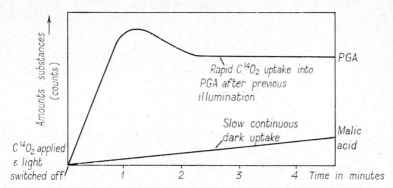

Fig. 3.7. The fixation of $C^{14}O_2$ to form PGA in the dark after a light period. (After Calvin.)

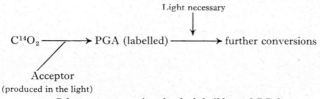

Scheme to summarize the dark build-up of PGA

able to combine with the carbon dioxide to form phosphoglyceric acid (PGA) even in the dark, until the acceptor is all used up. The PGA accumulates because some reaction which light usually catalyses can no longer take place in the dark, and this reaction is necessary for the removal of PGA. Figures 3.7 and 3.8 illustrate these relationships.

Identification of the carbon dioxide acceptor

Professor Calvin of the University of California was the first to sort out the sequence of the reactions and recognize the carbon dioxide acceptor. One of the spots formed on his chromatograms, obtained after a long light period, turned out to be a five-carbon sugar, *ribulose-diphosphate* (RDP). Analysis of the levels of RDP along with PGA and other intermediates (see fig. 3.8) showed that the level of RDP fell off sharply in the dark, indicating

† Small quantities of carbon dioxide are also fixed into malic acid.

that it was formed during active photosynthesis and was utilized in a dark reaction resulting in the formation of phosphoglyceric acid. A final and neat check experiment involved the removal of carbon dioxide from actively

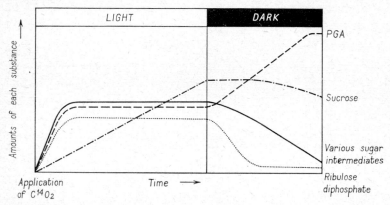

FIG. 3.8. The accumulation of labelled PGA and loss of labelled ribulose in the dark. (After Bassham, *J. Chem. Educ.*, November 1959.)

photosynthesizing *Scenedesmus* (see fig. 3·9). At once the level of PGA fell off while that of RDP rose sharply, as there was no carbon dioxide with which it could combine. When addition of this sugar was found to stimulate the uptake of carbon dioxide and the formation of PGA there was little doubt that this sugar was the carbon dioxide acceptor. Later Calvin was able to identify a specific enzyme, *carboxydismutase*, which catalysed

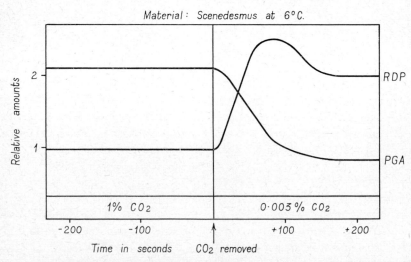

FIG. 3.9. The relative concentrations of PGA and ribulose in the light under different CO_2 concentrations. (After Bassham, *J. Chem. Educ.*, November 1959.)

this combination of carbon dioxide with the ribulose-diphosphate. One molecule of this five carbon sugar combines with one molecule of carbon dioxide (in the form of carbonic acid) to form two molecules of PGA. The following scheme shows how this change takes place:

$$
\begin{array}{ccc}
\mathrm{CH_2O}\!\!\left(\!\mathrm{P}\!\right) & & \mathrm{CH_2O}\!\!\left(\!\mathrm{P}\!\right) \\
| & & | \\
\mathrm{C=O} & & \mathrm{CHOH} \\
| & & | \\
\mathrm{CHOH} & & \mathrm{COOH} \\
| & +\,\mathrm{H_2CO_3} \longrightarrow & \\
\mathrm{CHOH} & & \mathrm{CH_2O}\!\!\left(\!\mathrm{P}\!\right) \\
| & & | \\
\mathrm{CH_2O}\!\!\left(\!\mathrm{P}\!\right) & & \mathrm{CHOH} \\
& & | \\
& & \mathrm{COOH}
\end{array}
$$

Ribulose-diphosphate + carbonic acid ⟶   2 molecules of phosphoglyceric acid

3.6   The photostage

It was mentioned above that PGA accumulated in the dark, and it was suggested that a light-requiring process took place in normal photosynthesis for the further conversion of PGA. Calvin showed that the conversion of PGA was the only light requiring reaction by sampling the various sugars and possible intermediates after a light followed by a dark period. He found that the concentration levels remained much the same or, more usually, fell off considerably—except the PGA, which accumulated. This was good evidence that there was only one light requiring reaction, otherwise other intermediates would also have accumulated. The graph, fig. 3.8, illustrates this experiment.

The next problem that Calvin dealt with was to find out the substances which were formed by the light reaction. His technique was a subtle one; he allowed the algae to photosynthesize in $C^{14}O_2$ for only a very short length of time and then analysed the results chromatographically. He then lengthened the time very slightly and re-analysed the products. By using a series of different light periods in this way and by comparing the results chromatographically he was able to suggest the possible sequence or pathway for substances produced as a result of the single light-requiring reaction. The initial products of the light reaction involved the three-carbon sugar, triose-phosphate:

$$
\begin{array}{c}
\mathrm{CH_2O}\!\!\left(\!\mathrm{P}\!\right) \\
| \\
\mathrm{CHOH} \\
| \\
\mathrm{CHO}
\end{array}
$$

(see autoradiographs, fig. 3.10). The further conversions of this three-carbon sugar to six-carbon and other sugars are not light requiring and are described under the final dark stage.

How, then, does light result in the conversion of a three-carbon acid (PGA) to a three-carbon sugar, triose-phosphate? It was stated in the general equation that water combined with carbon dioxide to form hexose, and so far scarcely any further mention of water has been made. It has

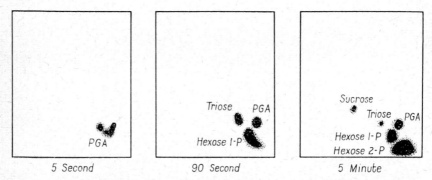

| 5 Second | 90 Second | 5 Minute |

FIG. 3.10. Autoradiographs of chromatograms showing C^{14} tracer distribution in extracts of algal cells, obtained after various light periods, in $C^{14}O_2$. (After Calvin.)

been found that the primary role of light, absorbed by the chloroplasts, is to provide the energy necessary for the splitting of the water molecule into hydrogen and oxygen. The hydrogen is required for the reduction of the carbon dioxide and the oxygen is released.

In 1940 Ruben showed that the oxygen given out in photosynthesis does indeed come from water and not, as was once believed, from carbon dioxide. This was shown by supplying the plant with water enriched with O^{18}, the heavy but non-radioactive isotope of oxygen. When oxygen released in photosynthesis was examined in the mass spectrometer—an apparatus capable of distinguishing between the isotopic forms—it was found that the gas contained a similar proportion of O^{18} to the water that was originally supplied. Enrichment of the carbon dioxide produced no corresponding enrichment in the oxygen produced.

Substrate	Period of O_2 collection in min. after start	Per cent O^{18} in		
		H_2O	$HCO_3^- + CO_3^=$	O_2
KHCO₃, 0·09 M	0	0·85	0·20	
K₂CO₃ 0·09 M	45–110	0·85	0·41	0·84
	110–225	0·85	0·55	0·85
	225–350	0·85	0·61	0·86

(After Thomas. *Plant Physiology*. London: J. & A. Churchill.)

Table to show isotopic ratio in oxygen evolved in photosynthesis by *Chlorella*. (After Ruben et al.)

This was clear evidence that the primary action of light was the splitting of the water molecule into hydrogen and oxygen. Investigation of the photostage must therefore consider both the role of the pigments in absorbing light and also the means by which the energy made available is used to split the water molecule and finally convert the PGA into triose-phosphate.

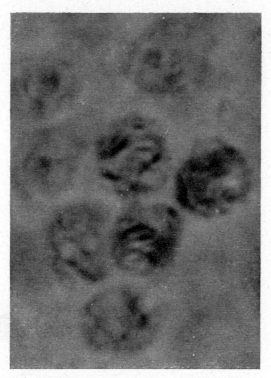

Fig. 3.11. Chloroplasts showing grana (*Lamium album*).
(Light microscope photograph.)

3.7 The role of the chloroplast pigments

The chloroplasts

We know that the chloroplasts are the site where photosynthesis occurs by examining tissues that have been photosynthesizing for the presence of starch grains; these are found around and inside the chloroplasts. If the chloroplasts are examined carefully under a high-power microscope the small, round grana of which they are composed may just be visible (fig. 3.11). Electron-microscope work has revealed that these minute grana are themselves made up of layers rather like a stack of coins; the layers are known to differ from one another in their pigment organization (see figs. 3.12 and 3.13). Clearly the chloroplasts and their grana are very highly organized structures, specially adapted for the absorbing of different wavelengths of light energy through the different pigments that they contain.

The pigments

If an extract of the chlorophyll pigments is made in pure acetone and carefully purified it can be analysed by chromatography to identify the pigments found. (For full details of the purification and chromatographic

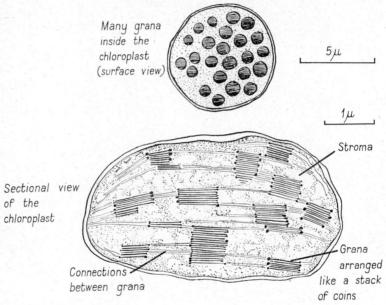

Many grana
inside the
chloroplast
(surface view)

5 μ

1 μ

Stroma

Sectional view
of the
chloroplast

Grana
arranged
like a stack
of coins

Connections
between grana

FIG. 3.12. The chloroplast showing the arrangement of the grana.

separation of the chlorophyll pigments see Appendix, p. 169.) Fig. 3.14 illustrates the resulting chromatogram. The yellow accessory pigment, carotene is least adsorbed and is found at the top of the paper behind the solvent front. Phaeophytin (grey, a breakdown product of chlorophyll), xanthophyll (yellow-green), chlorophyll *a* (blue-green) and chlorophyll *b* (yellow-green), as well as other pigments, should also appear. The identity of the pigments can be checked by comparing R_f values with those found in tables. After identification of the pigments by this method it is then possible to separate the pigments in solution so that their light-absorbing properties may be compared. This is best done by using a cellulose column (see fig. 3.15 and Appendix, p. 170). The solutions are rather unstable and should be examined immediately in the spectrometer.

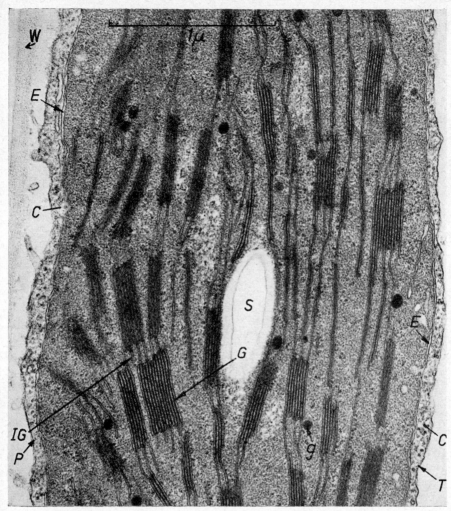

Fig. 3.13. Electron-microscope photograph of a section of a broad bean (*Vicia faba*) chloroplast. W = cell wall (there is a slight gap between the wall and the cytoplasm of the cell). P = plasmalemma (a single membrane). E = chloroplast envelope (this is clearly seen to include two membranes and it separates the chloroplast interior from the cytoplasm (C)). G = a granum (a stack-like unit formed where parts of several lamellae lie in close contact with each other). *I.G.* = intergranum lamellae. (These are parts of lamellae lying separately in the stroma. Each lamella consists of a pair of closely set membranes and they are continuous with the granal lamellae.) g = a droplet or globule of lipid in the chloroplast stroma. S = a grain of starch in the stroma. (The grains possess two well-marked zones which differ in composition. There is probably no enclosing membrane.) T = tonoplast. (Courtesy of Mr. A. D. Greenwood, Imperial College, London.)

Absorption spectra of the chlorophylls

The spectrometer must first be calibrated; this is most easily done using the mercury-vapour spectrum (see Appendix, p. 170). The total extracts as well as the separate pigments can then be examined. The results are

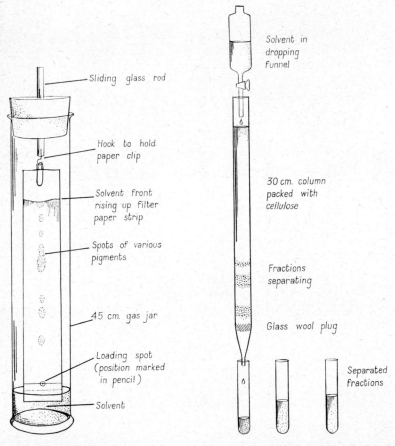

FIG. 3.14. Apparatus used for filter-paper strip chromatography.

FIG. 3.15. Apparatus used for column chromatography.

best recorded graphically, and it is interesting to note how the absorption bands of the individual pigments combine in the absorption spectrum produced from the total extract. Fig. 3.16 illustrates the absorption bands with total nettle extract and the most important green pigment chlorophyll *a*. It should be noted that the absorption bands using petroleum extract are found to be displaced slightly towards the blue end of the spectrum as

compared with the spectrum bands obtained by examining the living leaf
or a chloroplast suspension.

Reactions of the light stage

From the above results it is seen that the chlorophyll pigments absorb
light over a considerable range of the spectrum, but most from the red and
blue ends. The problem is, how is this absorbed light energy used to affect
the PGA–triose-phosphate conversion? It seems likely that the energy is
absorbed by the pigments and is transferred to chlorophyll *a*, which is regarded as the fundamental chlorophyll pigment. The fact that chlorophyll

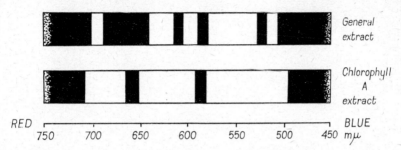

General
extract

Chlorophyll
A
extract

RED   BLUE
750   700   650   600   550   500   450 mμ

Fig. 3.16. Absorption spectra of some of the chlorophyll pigments.

extracts are strongly fluorescent, especially in ultra-violet light (see Appendix, p. 171), is visual evidence of the absorption of one wavelength of light
and emission of light of another wavelength. Fluorescence occurs partly
because the extracted pigments absorb light energy but are unable to transfer
it to normal energy acceptors; in consequence the light is simply re-emitted.
In the intact plant transference of energy from one pigment to another is
possible, provided the pigment particles are sufficiently close together;
electron microscopy has revealed that the pigments in the lamellae of
layers of the grana are probably sufficiently near one another.

All the energy absorbed is not necessarily utilized in the PGA–triose
conversion; if the absorption spectrum of a plant is compared with the
actual amount of photosynthesis (the 'action spectrum') by means of a
graph, then the two curves may not completely coincide. Data from the
sea lettuce *Ulva* (see fig. 3.17) shows that near 480 mμ absorption is relatively high compared with the amount of photosynthesis occurring; this is
due to some absorption by carotene pigments which is not fully utilized in
photosynthesis. Once the energy is absorbed it is mainly used, however,
for the breaking down of water into oxygen, which is released, and hydrogen, which is utilized in the PGA–triose conversion. Some evidence
regarding the mechanism of these stages comes from the Hill reaction.

The Hill reaction

In 1935 Hill, at Cambridge, found that isolated chloroplast suspensions, when illuminated, possessed the power to reduce ferric ions and at the same time produced oxygen. These chloroplast extracts could not utilize carbon dioxide, and in consequence it was assumed that the primary role of the illuminated chloroplasts, on their own, was to split water into oxygen, which was released, and hydrogen. In the *Hill reaction,* as this process has

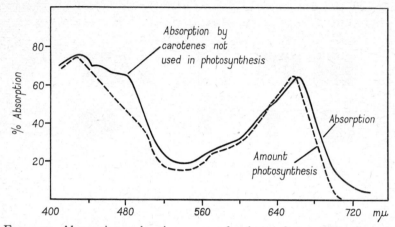

FIG. 3.17. Absorption and action spectra for the sea lettuce (*Ulva lactuca.*)
The curves are adjusted so as to correspond at 645 mμ. (After Thomas: *Plant Physiology.* London: J. &. A. Churchill.)

been called, the hydrogen must be accepted by an oxidizing agent; in early work such substances as potassium ferricyanide were used. For instance, the chloroplast extracts of beet and spinach are able to carry out the reaction as follows:

$$4\ Fe^{+++} + 2H_2O \xrightarrow[\text{chloroplasts}]{\text{light}} 4Fe^{++} + 4[H]^+ + O_2$$

More recently the redox dye 2:6 dichlorophenolindophenol has been extensively used (see Appendix, p. 172). This is bleached (or reduced) in a few minutes by illuminated chloroplast suspensions, showing that the latter have considerable *reducing power.* In the early 1940's Warburg found that chloride ions had a stimulating effect on the Hill reaction. It has been suggested that they may be important in allowing for the release of oxygen from hydroxyl ions. This may be the reason for the essential requirement of chloride ions by green plants.

The next problem was to find out how the reaction took place with reference to the whole photosynthetic process. It was thought likely that some hydrogen acceptor was able to transfer the hydrogen released by the splitting of the water molecule so as to carry out the PGA–triose phosphate reduction. The coenzyme triphosphopyridine nucleotide (TPN or CO II)† seemed a likely substance, and when this was added to illuminated, isolated chloroplasts a great increase in the rate of oxygen production took place (see fig. 3.18). Although several other enzymes and coenzymes can

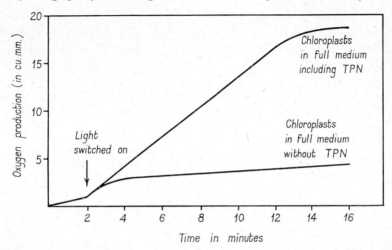

FIG. 3.18. Production of oxygen by chloroplasts in the Hill reaction. Effect of TPN on the rate of oxygen production. (After Arnon (1951). *Nature*, **167**, p. 1008.)

act as hydrogen donors and acceptors, it seems likely that only coenzyme I (diphosphopyridine nucleotide, DPN) may also be involved. Co-operation of metal–oxidase enzymes such as ascorbic acid, which can also act as donors of hydrogen, is ruled out, as these are inhibited by potassium cyanide (which forms stable complexes with their metal ions) and cyanide causes no inhibition of Hill-type reactions.

Photophosphorylation

In 1960 D. I. Arnon and his associates at the University of California showed that the light reaction may be coupled to other important reactions in addition to the simple splitting of the water molecules and formation of reduced nucleotides. In the presence of inorganic phosphate and adenosine diphosphate (ADP), adenosine triphosphate (ATP), 'high energy phosphate' may be formed. ATP formation is the main method that plants possess for transferring energy, and most of it is formed during the process of respiration (see p. 78), but it is particularly interesting that some should be synthesized directly in photosynthesis.

† Now often called Nicotinamide adenine dinucleotide (NAD).

3.8   The final dark stage

There are essentially two sets of conversions involved in the final dark stage. The first is concerned with the formation of the higher carbohydrate products, such as glucose, sucrose and starch, while the second is a series of reactions required to produce the five-carbon sugar, ribulose-diphosphate, the carbon dioxide acceptor which must be regenerated if the photosynthetic carbon cycle is to function. The various sequences of reactions involved here have been worked out by Calvin using the technique described above (see p. 46), in which algae are allowed to photosynthesize

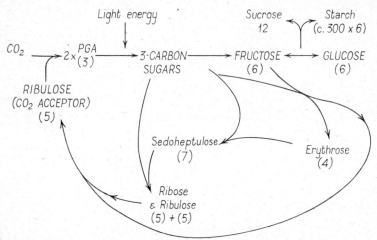

Scheme to show how the various carbohydrate intermediates co-operate in the photosynthetic carbon cycle.

The numbers under each sugar indicate the numbers of carbon atoms in each molecule. Each sugar contains either one or two phosphate groups.

for varying light periods in an atmosphere of $C^{14}O_2$. Autoradiographs of the products after periods of five seconds, ninety seconds and five minutes are shown in fig. 3.10, p. 50. These illustrate how, as the PGA (formed in the dark) is used up, first triose-phosphate, then hexose-1-phosphate, and finally sucrose, are formed. These are simplified autoradiographs, but by comparing the accumulation of intermediates in the different chromatograms and also by examining these for their distribution of C^{14} within the molecule, Calvin was able to show the main steps in both hexose and ribulose-diphosphate formation. It can also be shown that the formation of the higher carbohydrate starch from glucose is possible in the absence of light by a simple experiment (see Appendix, p. 176).

3.9   Summary

The process by which plants synthesize carbohydrates, utilizing water and carbon dioxide, is seen to be complex and divisible into four main phases:

the diffusion stage, the combination stage, the photostage and the final dark stages. It must be understood that these stages, though some may be able to operate in the dark, do, under normal circumstances, all take place at once in photosynthesizing tissues.

In conclusion it must be re-emphasized that photosynthesis is a process of fundamental importance to practically all living things, as it provides them with the energy that they require for life; in addition, it is the process that allowed for the vast Coal Age forests to grow and provide us with coal and oil, just as it is nowadays the process on which nearly all living things ultimately depend for food. In this respect the magnitude of the process should not be overlooked. For instance, it has been estimated that the forests of the world produce per annum something in the neighbourhood of 11 billion kgm. of organic carbon materials by photosynthesis. More precise information is available on the synthesis of sugars by a field of maize; Transeau in 1926 estimated the total glucose manufactured per acre to be 8,732 kgm. Even so, it is likely that the efficiency of photosynthesis as a means for capturing and utilizing sunlight is relatively low, being in the order of only 1 or 2 per cent.

Because of this apparent inefficiency, photosynthesis is a process which is of more than theoretical interest, as knowledge of its reactions and the way they operate may one day provide us with some methods through which normal agricultural photosynthetic production may be improved.

E

4   Respiration

4.1   The process

In the last chapter we dealt with the process by which green plants manufacture various carbohydrate food substances, incorporating the sun's energy into the plant. Respiration is a reversal of photosynthesis in that it is the means by which the food materials, such as glucose and fructose, are broken down into simpler substances, releasing energy in the process. The energy released is hardly evident externally (except in the form of some heat), as it is channelled into other systems and finally used for the various energy-requiring reactions going on within the plant. As no organism can do without energy, which it needs for these general processes of metabolism, respiration, like photosynthesis, is a vital process in living organisms.

By measurement of the volumes of the gases required and evolved and by the study of the conditions and requirements of the process the following general equation for the breakdown of hexose sugar is often written:

$$6O_2 + C_6H_{12}O_6 = 6CO_2 + 6H_2O$$

This kind of respiration, utilizing oxygen, is the means by which most plants and animals obtain a great part of their energy, and is called *aerobic respiration*. On the other hand, many plant tissues under conditions of low oxygen availability obtain their energy *anaerobically*. The following equation summarizes this process:

$$C_6H_{12}O_6 = 2CO_2 + 2C_2H_5OH$$

Instead of complete breakdown of the hexose to carbon dioxide and water taking place, ethanol and carbon dioxide are formed. Plants are unable to utilize this ethanol, which therefore represents a considerable wastage of energy, aerobic respiration being more than twelve times more efficient a process. In addition, small concentrations of alcohol are toxic and so most plants are unable to tolerate anaerobic conditions for long periods.

Extensive research using the techniques of chromatography, autoradiography and inhibitor treatments have revealed that respiration, like photosynthesis, is a many-stage process, and the general equations given above

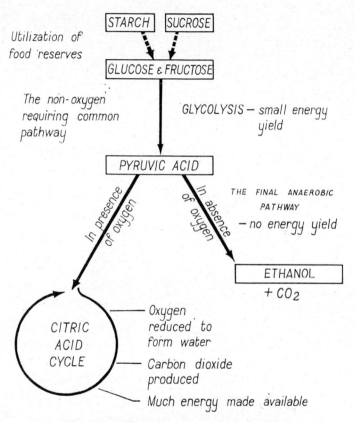

FIG. 4.1. The main stages of respiration.

are simply extreme summaries of what goes on. Work has shown that aerobic and anaerobic respiration share a common, non-oxygen requiring, pathway called *glycolysis* in their first stages, that is, in the breakdown of hexose into the simple three-carbon acid, pyruvic acid ($CH_3 \cdot CO \cdot COOH$). If oxygen is present, then the pyruvic acid is utilized through a series of conversions involving several tricarboxylic acids; this sequence is known as the *Krebs*, or *Citric Acid Cycle*. At various stages during the cycle oxygen is required and water and carbon dioxide released, energy being made

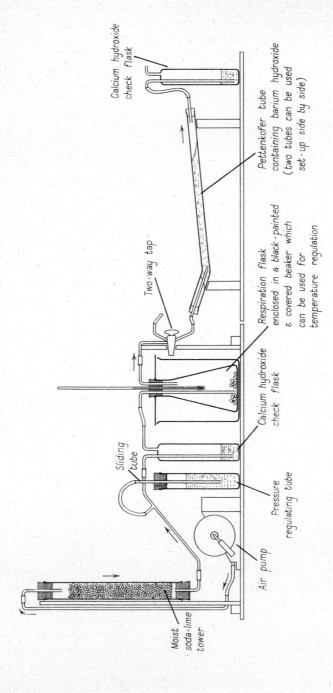

Calcium hydroxide check flask

Pettenkofer tube containing barium hydroxide (two tubes can be used set-up side by side)

Two-way tap

Respiration Flask enclosed in a black-painted & covered beaker which can be used for temperature regulation

Calcium hydroxide check flask

Sliding tube

Pressure regulating tube

Air pump

Moist soda-lime tower

FIG. 4.2. The Pettenkofer apparatus.

Used for the quantitative estimation of the carbon dioxide produced in respiration.

available in the process. On the other hand, if there is no oxygen a 'switch' occurs and the anaerobic sequence takes place, resulting in the production of alcohol. These stages are summarized in fig. 4.1.

In considering respiration there are two main lines of approach; first, that involving the effect of various factors on the rate of respiration of whole tissues or intact organisms, and secondly, that involving extraction of the individual substances concerned in the process and investigation of their properties; these are the biochemical aspects.

4.2 Measurement of the rate of respiration

A considerable amount can be learned about both the biology of the intact plant and the nature of the respiratory process itself through studies of the rate of respiration. The rate can be measured either in terms of oxygen uptake or of carbon dioxide production.

Measurement of carbon dioxide production

The Pettenkofer technique (see fig. 4.2) is used to measure the quantity of carbon dioxide produced by a given weight or volume of material in a given time. Essentially, carbon-dioxide-free air is supplied to the respiring material and the respiratory gases passed into baryta (barium hydroxide). The carbon dioxide reacts with the baryta to form insoluble barium carbonate. After a given period the unchanged baryta is titrated against standard hydrochloric acid using phenol phthalein as indicator to find how much

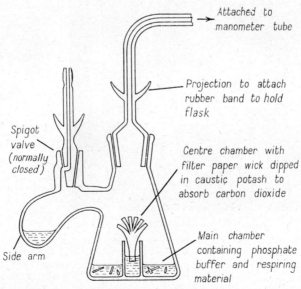

Attached to manometer tube

Projection to attach rubber band to hold flask

Spigot valve (normally closed)

Centre chamber with filter paper wick dipped in caustic potash to absorb carbon dioxide

Side arm

Main chamber containing phosphate buffer and respiring material

FIG. 4.3. The flask of the Warburg manometer.

baryta is left, and hence how much of the baryta has been used up by re-action with the carbon dioxide. From this value the amount of carbon di-oxide produced per unit of respiring material per hour can be calculated (see Appendix, p. 177).

The Pettenkofer apparatus can be used to compare the rate of respira-tion of various whole plants, or to investigate changes in respiratory rate during plant growth or senescence, for instance, during germination. The apparatus can also be used to measure the effect of various factors, such as temperature or oxygen availability, on the rate of the process.

Measurement of oxygen uptake

The Warburg manometric method is the most useful for determining the rate of oxygen uptake. In this device (see figs. 4.3, and 4.4) the respir-

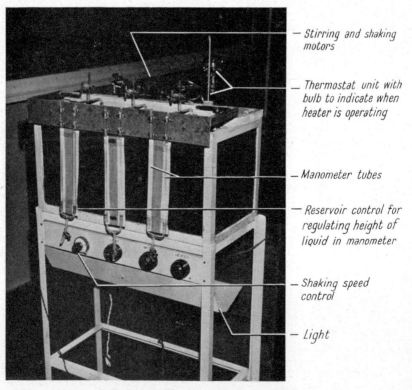

— Stirring and shaking motors

— Thermostat unit with bulb to indicate when heater is operating

— Manometer tubes

— Reservoir control for regulating height of liquid in manometer

— Shaking speed control

— Light

FIG. 4.4. The Warburg manometer.

This device is used for the estimation of gas exchange by respiring or photo-synthesizing tissues. The apparatus consists of a temperature-controlled water-bath together with a set of three or more flask and manometer units. The flasks are sub-merged in the tank and kept shaken by a motor. The glass bottom of the tank allows for illumination of photosynthesizing material. This is a home-made version of the apparatus which has been found to give quite satisfactory results.

ing material is enclosed in a small flask and kept at a constant temperature in a thermostatically controlled water-bath. A small manometer is attached to the flask, and this registers any gases produced or taken up. Caustic potash can be included in the centre well to absorb carbon dioxide as it is produced so that the apparatus is able to record the amount of oxygen utilized. The flask is also provided with a side arm from which inhibitors or special substrates can be added once the normal rate of respiration of the material has been determined. A blank, control manometer, the thermo-barometer, is also run alongside to make correction for any temperature or barometric change. For full details of the technique see Appendix on p. 179.

Respiratory quotient

Some information about the substrates being used in respiration and also the type of respiration in progress may be obtained by comparing the

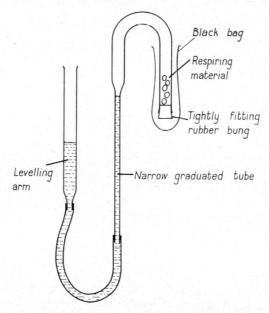

FIG. 4.5. A simple Ganong respirometer.

Two sets of apparatus are needed, one with caustic potash to absorb CO_2, one with water in the tube. For example, after 48 hours the RQ of germinating peas was found as follows:

(1) + KOH: 8·0 ml. O_2 consumed
(2) + H_2O: 2·5 ml. CO_2 produced in excess of O_2 consumed
∴ CO_2 produced = 10.5 c.c.
∴ $RQ = \dfrac{CO_2}{O_2} = \dfrac{10·5}{8·0} = 1·33$

A control respirometer using water, but no peas, should also be set up to allow for any temperature and barometric changes.

amount of carbon doxide produced with oxygen utilized. The respiratory quotient is the amount of carbon dioxide produced divided by the amount of oxygen utilised over a given period of time.

$$RQ \;=\; \frac{\text{Volume } CO_2 \text{ produced}}{\text{Volume } O_2 \text{ absorbed}}$$

RQs for the complete oxidation of various respirable substrates, which can be calculated from the equation for the complete oxidation of the substance concerned to carbon dioxide, are given in the table below:

	RQ	Material
	0·7	Fats
	1·0	Carbohydrates
About	0·9	Proteins and amino-acids

In practice, these values are seldom obtained exactly, as complete oxidation rarely occurs and there may be a mixture of substrates being

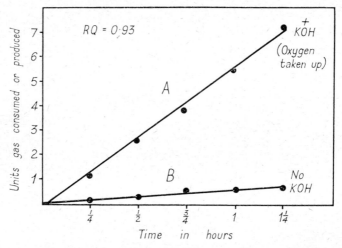

Fig. 4.6. Manometric estimation of respiratory quotient of barley root tips.

A = oxygen taken up
B = excess oxygen taken up over carbon dioxide produced

$$RQ = \frac{\text{vol. } CO_2}{\text{vol. } O_2} = \frac{7\cdot0 - 0\cdot5}{7\cdot0} = \frac{6\cdot5}{7\cdot0} = 0\cdot93 \quad \text{(Class result.)}$$

utilized. It can be demonstrated very simply that the RQ of normal germinating peas (which have a food reserve composed largely of carbohydrates) is near unity by placing the peas in the closed end of an inverted U-tube, the other, open, end of which is in water. If the peas are left for some time there should be no change in the level of the water in the tube. But if the open end of the tube is placed in caustic potash the liquid level will rise inside the tube, indicating absorption of carbon dioxide. Thus, as there is no change in level in the first case, in spite of carbon dioxide being produced, then the amount of carbon dioxide given out must be the same as the amount of oxygen utilized and the RQ = 1.

If the respiration chamber is connected to a manometer or volume-measuring device, then the RQ can be measured accurately, and this is the principle used in manometric experiments (figs. 4.4 and 4.6) and also in the Ganong respirometer (see Appendix, p. 178).

Respiratory quotients may also give some indication of the type of respiration going on. Clearly an RQ of 1 suggests the fully aerobic respiration of carbohydrates. High RQ values between 2 and 7 are found when the plant is respiring under water-logged, oxygen-deficient conditions. These suggest the occurrence of anaerobic respiration. Low RQs below 0·5 may indicate that some of the carbon dioxide is being fixed, perhaps to form plant acids (e.g. malic acid, see p. 47).

Production of heat and energy

The main production of energy in the respiratory process is utilized for the formation of high-energy phosphate, ATP, from ADP (see p. 78).

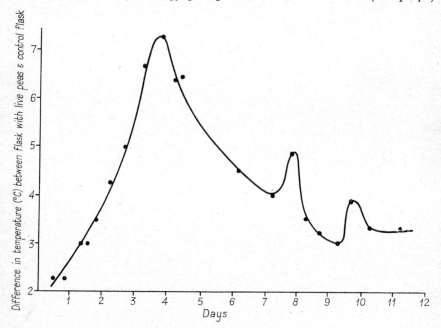

FIG. 4.7. Fluctuations in heat production of germinating peas. (Class result.)

In addition to this, some heat production, which is necessary to maintain a thermodynamic equilibrium, normally occurs, and this may be used to give some indication of the rate of respiration.

Temperature changes can be detected by placing the respiring material, such as germinating peas, in a thermos flask stoppered with cotton-wool and including a thermometer. A similar control can be set up using germinating peas that have been killed with boiling water and kept sterile by the addition of mercuric chloride to prevent bacterial infection. It is also best to surface sterilize the living peas to kill any bacteria and fungi that may be present. This is best carried out by soaking the peas in a 1 per cent solution of sodium hypochlorite for three minutes and then washing them in sterile distilled water. If the daily measurements of temperature are plotted on a graph the results illustrated in fig. 4.7 may be obtained. This illustrates that the amount of heat evolved rises as germination begins and does not fall off until most of the available substrates have been utilized.

4.3   The effect of various factors on the rate of respiration of the intact organism

Effect of oxygen concentration

The ability of different organisms to survive in different oxygen concentrations can be examined using the Pettenkofer technique. This is most simply carried out by providing the plant with nitrogen and oxygen

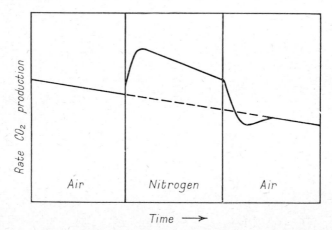

FIG. 4.8. The effect of nitrogen on the respiratory rate of apples. (After Blackman *Analytic: Studies in Plant Respiration*. Cambridge, University Press.)

from cylinders. Different oxygen concentrations can be provided by regulating the oxygen flow compared with the nitrogen flow. A pressure-regulating device, as used in the Pettenkofer set-up, should be fitted to both oxygen and nitrogen lines. For short periods the oxygen may be removed by passing the gas through two or three bottles containing alkaline pyrogallol.

On removal of oxygen the rate of respiration of the organism might be expected to fall off, but in most cases the rate, in terms of carbon dioxide production, actually increases. This indicates that anaerobic respiration comes into action when oxygen is no longer available and that the plant, if it is to make up for the relative inefficiency of this system, has to respire faster. The graph (fig. 4.8) illustrates this effect when apples are in air and nitrogen.

Unless the organism is particularly well adapted to life under low-oxygen concentrations, such treatment will in most cases probably result in the eventual death of the organism. Under natural conditions most plants are aerobic, but even in these there may be times, for instance in the root, when the soil is temporarily waterlogged, and some tissues respire anaerobically. Such organisms are referred to as facultative anaerobes, at least for the tissue concerned. Few plants are able to respire anaerobically for any length of time, a notable exception being the seedling of a rice plant, which is able to survive under completely anaerobic conditions for a considerable period. How far the roots of many marsh and semi-aquatic plants, although they often possess porous, *aerenchymatous* stems and roots, are able to stand up to anaerobic conditions is still largely unknown, and it is interesting to speculate whether such tolerances may be important in determining the competition and subsequent survival of plants in such communities. Better-known facultative anaerobes, such as yeast (*Saccharomyces cerevisiae*), can usually tolerate anaerobic conditions until the accumulation of the poisonous waste product ethanol, which is toxic at 12 per cent concentration, renders a return to aerobic conditions a necessity if the organism is to continue to live. Selection through the ages of good fermenting strains of yeast have enhanced its tolerance for alcohol, but it must be emphasized that in spite of this, it grows much better under aerobic conditions. A similar situation exists in the potato, but lactic acid is the waste product that accumulates. A few organisms, principally soil bacteria such as the *Clostridia*, are obligate anaerobes and can live in wet, clay soils.

Effect of substrate availability

If apples are placed in the respiratory chamber of the Pettenkofer apparatus and the amount of carbon dioxide produced per day measured over a period of months, then as the apples ripen and different substrates for respiration are made available, the respiratory rate changes.

Such an experiment is clearly rather laborious, but it does give general information on the substrates utilized in apple respiration. Simpler experiments can be done using fungi which grow quickly and can easily be cultured on a variety of substrates. The respiratory rate of colonies of similar size of the same fungus growing on different media, such as lignin, cellulose, starch and glucose, can be found. Investigations on these lines may be of considerable value in ecological studies.

Effect of temperature

Like most chemical reactions, the rate of respiration is influenced by temperature; the higher the temperature, the faster the rate. For instance, estimation of Q_{10} of the process (see above p. 43) for a rise in temperature from 8° to 18° C. gives a Q_{10} of 2, indicating a chemical reaction. But if the rise is at a much higher starting temperature, say between 20° and 30° C., then the Q_{10} may fall below 2. This is partly accounted for by the steps of respiration taking place so fast that the rate falls off, as the oxygen cannot diffuse into the leaf fast enough. In addition, substrate interconversions may take place at higher temperatures. For instance, fats may be formed from carbohydrates by a reaction in which carbon dioxide is utilised and oxygen produced. This will clearly upset the readings for the amount of respiratory carbon dioxide actually produced.

The effect of temperature on different plants is an obvious factor in determining plant distribution. Some plants are better adapted to life at higher temperature than others, and when growing in their most suitable temperature range are best able to compete with their neighbours. This is well illustrated by reference to the temperature required for germination of various seeds. A temperate mesophyte, hairy willow herb (*Epilobium hirsutum*), germinates best at about 21° C., wheat will germinate between 5° and about 34° C., while subtropical maize has a still higher temperature range.

4.4 Biochemical aspects: the anaerobic pathway

(i) *Glycolysis*

The ease with which most plants are able to switch from aerobic to anaerobic respiration and back is perhaps an indication that the processes are very closely related to one another in some of their stages. That they do indeed share a common pathway in part is shown by two main pieces of evidence. First, that the temperature coefficients or Q_{10}s for aerobic and anaerobic respiration are the same, indicating participation by some of the same enzymes at an early stage in both processes, and secondly, the use of the inhibitor sodium iodoacetate has shown that by blocking one reaction it is possible to inhibit both aerobic and anaerobic respiration. This substance inhibits the conversion of triose-phosphate into phosphoglyceric acid by the enzyme triose-phosphate dehydrogenase, which is an early stage in glycolysis. Other substances can be used to inhibit either aerobic or anaerobic respiration separately, which shows that in some stages at least the two processes must be quite different. This primary, anaerobic phase involves the breakdown of hexose sugar, in direct reversal of the photosynthetic sequence, through three-carbon sugars, including phosphoglyceraldehyde, to phosphoglyceric acid and finally pyruvic acid (see fig. 4.9). The individual steps of this process have been investigated by chromatographic and general analysis methods.

An important feature of glycolysis is that two hydrogen atoms must be removed. These are passed to a hydrogen acceptor (TPN), which becomes reduced. It is probable that this reaction is coupled with the synthesis of ATP from ADP. Two molecules of ATP are synthesized from ADP for every molecule of hexose sugar broken down; this represents a small release of energy which can be utilized by the plant.

(ii) *The final anaerobic pathway*

In the absence of oxygen the pyruvic acid, formed in glycolysis, is broken down to form acetaldehyde and finally ethanol. Carbon dioxide is produced in the first step, and is that which appears during fermentation processes:

$$
\begin{array}{ccc}
\underset{\text{pyruvic acid}}{\overset{\displaystyle CH_3}{\underset{\displaystyle COOH}{\overset{|}{\underset{|}{CO}}}}} \quad \overset{}{\underset{\displaystyle CO_2}{\searrow}} \longrightarrow &
\underset{\text{acetaldehyde}}{\overset{\displaystyle CH_3}{\underset{\displaystyle CHO}{\overset{|}{}}}} \xrightarrow{\; +\, 2[H] \;} &
\underset{\text{ethanol}}{\overset{\displaystyle CH_3}{\underset{\displaystyle OH}{\overset{|}{\underset{|}{CH_2}}}}}
\end{array}
$$

The Conway method (see Appendix, p. 182) can be used to demonstrate part of this pathway. If an active strain of yeast that has been living under aerobic conditions is fed with glucose in a closed Conway unit, acetaldehyde is formed which diffuses into the centre well of the flask, where its presence is detected by a dilute solution of 2:4-dinitrophenylhydrazine. The formation of ethanol can, of course, be demonstrated by distilling the product of anaerobic respiration.

Although no ATP is formed during this final anaerobic pathway, the importance of the reactions is that they allow for the acceptance of hydrogen. The reduced TPN, formed during glycolysis, can be reoxidized by passing the hydrogen to the acetaldehyde which becomes reduced to ethanol. In this way the TPN is made re-available for more glycolysis.

The net gain in ATP per molecule of hexose respired during the whole of anaerobic respiration is thus the two molecules of ATP formed during glycolysis.

4.5 Aerobic respiration: the Citric Acid Cycle

Analysis of acids

If some leaves that have been respiring in air are ground up they are usually found to produce an acid reaction when tested with indicators. Some of these acids can be found by means of chemical tests, and malic and citric acids are often identified (see Appendix, p. 182). Careful chromatographic analysis will reveal the presence of a wide range of acids.

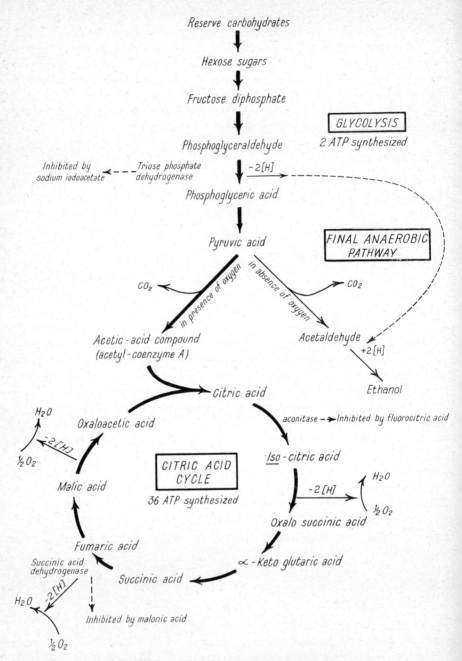

FIG. 4.9. The respiratory pathways.

These are mostly constituents of the *Citric Acid* or *Krebs Cycle* (see fig. 4.9), in which pyruvic acid is broken down in the presence of oxygen to yield carbon dioxide and water and bring about the formation of the main part of the plant's high-energy phosphate, ATP.

The evidence that has been used to show how a few steps of the cycle occur is discussed in the following sections.

Use of inhibitors

Inhibitor treatments have proved most useful in sorting out the individual steps in reaction pathways. In general, the principle behind the use of these substances is as follows. Suppose we have a reaction sequence which we believe, from other evidence (e.g. analysis of intermediates), to go A⟶B⟶C⟶D and we think that the reaction B⟶C is controlled by an enzyme for which there is a known inhibitor. Then if we examine and compare by analysis, the occurrence of these substances A, B, C and D before and after inhibition, the inhibited reaction should show much the same concentration of A, more than normal of B and the near absence of C and D. We would obtain confirmation that the reaction B⟶C has been inhibited by adding C and then detecting the additional presence of D.

One of the best examples of an inhibitor that has been useful in the study of the Citric Acid Cycle is malonic acid. This blocks the conversion of succinic acid into fumaric acid. This occurs because malonic acid has a structure which is superficially similar to that of succinic acid, so that it competes for reaction with the enzyme, succinic dehydrogenase, and the normal conversion of succinic acid into fumaric acid is slowed up. It is likely that the enzyme forms a complex with the malonic acid substrate; but due to the difficulty of removing hydrogen from this substance, it is unable to act and remains as a malonic acid–enzyme complex that effectively prevents the enzyme acting in the normal succinic–fumaric acid conversion.

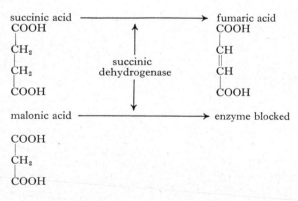

In the presence of malonic acid, succinic acid accumulates and the concentration of fumaric acid falls off—thus indicating one step in the cycle of acids.

Another inhibitor that has proved useful is fluoroacetic acid, for this blocks the enzyme aconitase which is required in the conversion of citric acid into *isocitric* acid. Fluoroacetic acid has a structure that is similar to acetic acid except that it has one hydrogen atom of the methyl group replaced by fluorine. It is converted into fluorocitric acid by the condensing enzyme which would normally function in the conversion of oxaloacetic acid and acetyl coenzyme A (an 'acetic acid compound') into citric acid. The enzyme aconitase, which would, in the normal cell, convert the citric acid into *isocitric* acid, is now unable to utilize fluorocitric acid, and thus an inhibition of respiration follows. Through the accumulation of fluorocitric acid by inhibition another step in the Citric Acid Cycle has been indicated. It is also interesting, as it illustrates the specificity of an enzyme; in the first reaction the enzyme has a wide specificity and is unable to distinguish between acetic and fluoroacetic acid, but the second enzyme (aconitase) is more specific, and no conversion of the alien substance follows. These relationships are summarized below and in fig. 4.9.

(*a*) *In the normal cell*

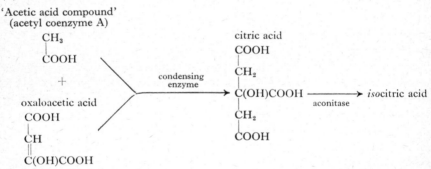

(*b*) *With the inhibitor*

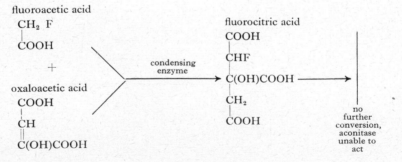

Use of radioactive tracers

A good example of the use of radioactive tracers in the study of aerobic respiration comes from feeding tissues with labelled pyruvic acid. If the carbon atom of the carboxyl group is labelled with C^{14}, then no tracer appears in the acids of the Citric Acid Cycle when they are examined by chromatograms and autoradiographs. On the other hand, the carbon dioxide produced is highly radioactive. Labelling in the methyl or carbonyl group results in a considerable accumulation of tracer in the acids of the cycle and relatively little in the carbon dioxide. This is direct evidence that the first step in the cycle is one which involves carbon dioxide production as well as indicating that pyruvic acid is the starting-point of the cycle of acids.

Addition of labelled acids of the cycle and detection of their conversion into other acids has also proved a fruitful line of research, and by the use of tracers and inhibitors, chromatographic and autoradiographic means, the main steps of the cycle have been worked out. Pyruvic acid is seen to be completely oxidized—that is, all its hydrogen atoms are removed, oxaloacetic acid being successively used and regenerated.

4.6   The oxidase systems

The next problem is how are these hydrogen atoms removed and the oxygen utilized? Another inhibitor, perhaps the best known of all, potassium cyanide, has been found useful here; it considerably reduces aerobic respiration (see fig. 4.10) by blocking the oxidase enzymes that are responsible for transferring hydrogen to atmospheric oxygen. These

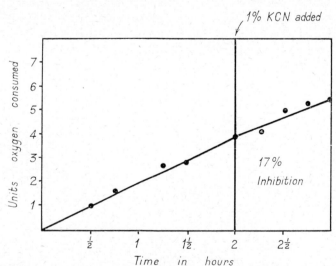

FIG. 4.10. The effect of KCN on the respiration of barley root tips.
(Class result.)

F

oxidase enzymes are part of *redox-chains*, oxidation–reduction systems, in which not only the hydrogen but also electrons are transferred from a substrate so that the reduction of oxygen to form water may ultimately take place. These chains have a number of stages. First, an enzyme (a dehydrogenase) removes hydrogen and an electron from the substrate, secondly, a non-protein *coenzyme* accepts these so that the enzyme is oxidized back to its original state, ready to react with more substrate. At the next stage of the redox-chain the electron causes the reduction of a *carrier enzyme* and the hydrogen ion may be released to the surroundings. This carrier enzyme then transfers its electron to a *terminal oxidase* which then reduces oxygen, so that, with the released hydrogen ion, water is formed. These steps can be summarized as follows:

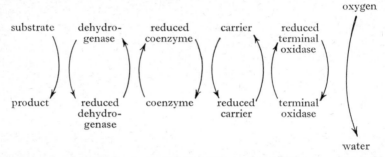

Common coenzymes include DPN (diphosphopyridine nucleotide) and TPN (triphosphopyridine nucleotide); cytochrome *c* and ascorbic acid (vitamin C) are common carriers. Some terminal oxidases are cytochrome oxidase, ascorbic oxidase and polyphenol oxidase. A good example of a redox-chain occurs in conjunction with the succinic acid to fumaric acid conversion, a reaction which requires the removal of two hydrogen ions and two electrons. † In this case there is no coenzyme and the dehydrogenase is able to pass its electrons directly to cytochrome *c*.

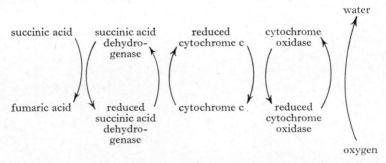

Inhibition by cyanide is usually indicative of the presence of a metallic group in the enzyme concerned, and in the terminal oxidases it is either

† See Appendix, p. 183–184 for experiments.

copper or iron. Cyanide forms stable complexes with these metals, thus blocking the enzyme. In the cytochromes iron is the metal concerned in the electron transfer system; this can be shown by the use of carbon monoxide, which inhibits respiration in the dark but not in the light. This is because only iron–carbon monoxide complexes are light sensitive. The ascorbic acid and polyphenol oxidase systems contain copper as their metallic or activator group. It is interesting that these transition elements copper and iron play such an important part in respiration, the enzymes concerned depending on the ability of these metals to become successively oxidized and reduced.

The full equation for the conversion of succinic acid into fumaric acid would therefore take place as follows:

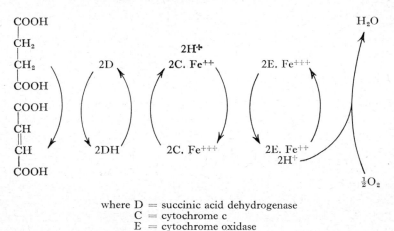

where D = succinic acid dehydrogenase
C = cytochrome c
E = cytochrome oxidase

Investigation of the cytochromes

We have seen above that the cytochromes and other oxidase systems have a vital position in respiration, and an understanding of how they occur and function is an important aspect of respiratory studies. If the extracts prepared from young and actively growing plants are examined spectroscopically (yeasts, onions and shallots make particularly good sources, see Appendix, p. 185) it is usual to find a series of weak absorption bands. Under reducing conditions these may be intensified, and under oxidising conditions they nearly disappear. These absorption bands (see fig. 4.11) are due to various cytochromes, the most distinct band is found at 550 mμ and indicates the presence of the most abundant and widely occurring cytochrome, cytochrome c. These substances may also be identified in tissue extracts by their reaction with Nadis' reagent (Appendix, p. 205), which turns a pinkish-purple if cytochromes are present. The Cytochromes *a*, *b* and *c* act readily as carriers, as described above, in accepting electrons from dehydrogenase enzymes so that cytochrome oxidase, the terminal oxidase, may become oxidized by atmospheric oxygen.

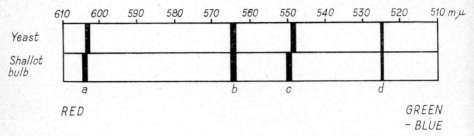

FIG. 4.11. Absorption spectra of the cytochromes.

Each cytochrome has α, β, and γ bands; *a*, *b*, and *c* are the α-bands of cytochromes *a*, *b*, *c*, the band of cytochrome *c* being much the strongest. β bands appear towards the blue end of the spectrum about 525 mμ at *d*; γ bands are found around 430 mμ.

4.7   Oxidative phosphorylation

The glycolysis sequence includes two steps in which high-energy phosphate (ATP) is synthesized from ADP by non-oxidative steps; in the aerobic system a further thirty-six molecules of ATP are synthesized for each molecule of hexose respired. The problem is, how is this vital synthesis carried out? The answer is still by no means certain, but it is likely that a large amount of free energy (8,000 cal./mole) is made available at each of two or three steps in each electron transfer chain. This energy is sufficient to allow for the formation of a high-energy phosphate bond. As the electrons flow from one substance to the next in the chain, the energy is transferred to the phosphorylation of ADP. This table summarizes the ATP formation in the breakdown of pyruvic acid by the Citric Acid Cycle:

Reaction	*Molecules ATP synthesized*
1. Oxidative decarboxylation of pyruvic acid	3
2. *Isocitric* ⟶ oxalosuccinic	3
3. Oxidative decarboxylation of α-ketoglutaric acid	4
4. Succinic acid ⟶ fumaric acid	2
5. Malic acid ⟶ oxaloacetic acid	3
Total	15

As two molecules of pyruvic acid are oxidized for each molecule of hexose utilized, this gives a total of thirty molecules of ATP produced through the aerobic stages of respiration. The full total is thirty-eight molecules of ATP, two being produced during glycolysis and the remaining six being derived from the *oxidation* of the reduced coenzyme formed in the conversion of triose into phosphoglyceric acid. In effect, thirty-six molecules of ATP are synthesized by the aerobic steps.

The high-energy phosphate system has been evolved in living things as a device for storing and moving energy; through this system they are able to provide the energy for growth, synthesis and movement that is the very essence of metabolism.

4.8   The site of respiration in the cell

Recently attention has been focused on the properties and organization of the various minute organelles within the cell. Phase-contrast films of

0·5 μ

FIG. 4.12. The mitochondrion.

cell-division usually show a very considerable activity of the small cigar-shaped bodies called mitochondria near the spindle of the dividing cell. These mitochondria show a very active jostling movement—rather more than would be expected to occur through Brownian movement alone—and it is possible that they are congregating where considerable energy may be needed in the process of cell-division. That they have an important part in cell activities, as the site of many respiratory enzymes and also of the high-energy phosphate synthesis system, has been shown by two main lines of research. In the first, bulk extracts of the mitochondria have been made and their properties examined; in the second, very thin sections have been photographed in the electron microscope and the structure of the mitochondria examined in detail.

The existence of the mitochondria has been known for many years, as in addition to phase-contrast studies, they may also be stained, though rather unevenly, by Janus Green B. Such staining has revealed the mitochondrion to be a minute elongated organelle about 0·7–1 μ in length. In spite of their small size, mitochondria can be extracted in bulk by fractional centrifuging. The first job is to extract the mitochondria as far as possible intact and undamaged. This can be done by careful grinding of the cells of the material using an ice-cold mixture of sucrose and phosphate buffer. This solution should have a slightly higher osmotic pressure than that of the original cell sap so as to prevent osmotic destruction of the organelles. The mitochondria are thrown down between 10,000 and 20,000 ×g., and after resuspension in buffer and washing by more gentle centrifuging are ready for examination.

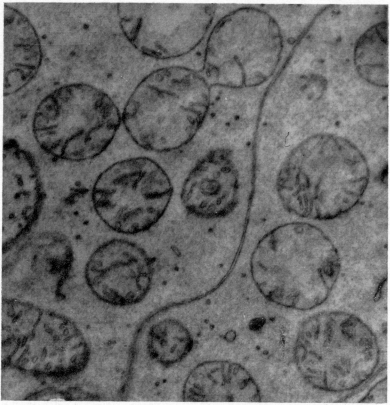

FIG. 4.13. Mitochondria from the root tip of barley; electron microscope photograph. (× 23,000.) (Courtesy of Dr. B. E. Juniper.)

Chemical analysis has shown them to be largely protein (30–40 per cent) and fat (25–38 per cent), the remainder being composed mostly of ribonucleic acid (RNA); spectroscopic analysis has shown also that the mitochondria are rich in the cytochromes. Addition of pyruvic acid to the preparation of mitochondria results in its oxidation, while addition of radioactively labelled succinic acid, with chromatographic and autoradiographic analysis, shows the presence of labelled fumaric, malic and citric acids. Therefore the mitochondria probably have most of the enzyme systems of the Citric Acid Cycle, though it is of course possible that other parts of the cell also produce similar enzymes. A most interesting and important feature of the mitochondria is that adenosine-diphosphate and free phosphate ions seem to be necessary for their efficiency in oxidation; they are in fact the site where the ATP is synthesized.

Electron-microscope photographs of ultra-thin sections of mitochondria (see figs. 1.1, 4.13, 6.8 and 6.9) have shown them to be composed of a thin outer membrane and a more complex inner system composed of channels called *cristae* running into the inner part of the organelle. Some idea of how and where these vital respiratory steps take place has been gained from autoradiographs taken after feeding with radioactive intermediates. Another technique, using tellurium oxide or tellurite has also proved useful. The oxide is reduced to the metal (which is dense to electrons and appears black in electron-microscope photographs) by the action of the reduced succinic dehydrogenase formed in the succinic acid–fumaric acid reaction in the Citric Acid Cycle. Accordingly, wherever the succinic acid reaction takes place, black specks of tellurium metal may be expected, and indeed these are found lining the cristae of the mitochondrion. It seems likely that these indentations may be the site where the vital steps of respiration, resulting in the formation of ATP, take place. As electron transfer systems are vital to these steps, it is thought that the arrangement of the cristae is such as to allow ready exchange of electrons between enzyme and substrate by providing a suitable space for electron transfer to take place.

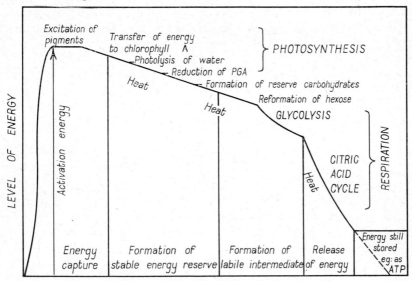

FIG. 4.14. The energy relationships of the plant.

The captions under the curve indicate energy loss that is necessitated by the laws of thermodynamics.

4.9 Summary and importance of respiration

Respiration consists in its early stages of a reversal of photosynthesis; the hexose sugar (fructose-diphosphate) is broken down through three carbon sugars to phosphoglyceric acid, and this is eventually converted into pyruvic acid. Little energy in the form of ATP is made available in this anaerobic process of glycolysis. The process is rather a rearrangement of the molecules concerned into a position from which efficient breakdown resulting in the formation of high-energy phosphate can take place. In the anaerobic system two molecules of ATP are synthesized for each molecule of hexose originally utilized, while in the aerobic Citric Acid Cycle system thirty-six molecules of ATP are synthesized for each molecule of hexose. This illustrates the much greater efficiency, in terms of ATP synthesis, of the aerobic system. The actual efficiency of energy yield in aerobic respiration is surprisingly high, being about 67 per cent.

The energy relationships of the plant can be summarized into four main phases (see fig. 4.14). In the first place the sun's energy is captured by the photosynthetic pigments. Secondly, the energy is stored in *stable* complex organic substances. Thirdly, these substances are modified into *labile* forms (e.g. pyruvic acid) which can be broken down to release energy, which is transferred to form ATP. At each step some energy is lost—a necessity in terms of the second law of thermodynamics—but the net effect is that the ATP is formed which is capable of activating further energy-requiring processes.

The fascinating part of respiration undoubtedly concerns the formation of this substance, and interest in respiration is now directed towards unravelling the mechanism through which this occurs.

5   Mineral Nutrition

5.1   Minerals and the soil

One of the main factors influencing plant distribution is the type of soil. In the British Isles there are a number of more or less clearly defined soil types. One of the simplest of these is the *rendzina*. This is found on chalk and limestone rocks, where the humus layer is thin and lies directly on the rock substrate. Such a soil is kept in this state by the rapid-draining, porous nature of the rock, which keeps the humus layers dry and aerated and so promotes the oxidation of the decaying material. A chalk soil, being so close to the parent rock, is rich in minerals, particularly calcium and magnesium ions, but on the other hand, the high pH may render other minerals insoluble. For instance, the important elements iron and manganese are relatively unavailable to plants.

The group of plants that are adapted to living under such soil conditions are called *calcicoles*. Typical plants in this group include the upright brome (*Bromus erectus*), small scabious (*Scabiosa columbaria*), salad burnet (*Poterium sanguisorba*) and squinancywort (*Asperula cynanchica*). These are well adapted to life on calcareous soils, as they have low demands for iron and manganese. Many calcicoles can, however, live in acid soils provided aluminium is absent. This element is more readily available on soils of low pH and if absorbed by calcicoles may prevent them growing.

A complete contrast is the *podsol* soil found in sand and gravelly areas. Here the soil is open and porous, but there are relatively few minerals present and these are easily washed or leached out of the soil by the rain. High humidity may favour the accumulation of undecayed humus, which is acid and aggravates the leaching effect. On these acid soils calcium and magnesium have usually been dissolved away, but iron and manganese are freely available, the latter being in the readily absorbed bivalent state.

Sometimes too much manganese may be available, which may have a toxic effect. Plants which are adapted to life on acid soils of this sort are called *calcifuges*. Ling (*Calluna vulgaris*), heath bedstraw (*Galium saxatile*) and the grass *Holcus mollis* are in this class. These plants have high demands for potassium and phosphate ions, which are less readily absorbed in the presence of calcium ions, which tend to antagonize their uptake. In addition, they can tolerate the aluminium level of the soil and have fair demands for the readily available iron and manganese.

The most suitable soil for agriculture lies half-way between these two soil types. This is the *brown earth*. This type of soil is usually found on clays or rich sands and has a pH near neutrality, about 6·5. Here there is a fair balance between the mineral content, the accumulation of humus and the water content, so that a reasonable quantity of dissolved ions are available to plants. Such soils support the rich vegetation of the natural oak woods, but nowadays they are mostly exploited as arable land.

These general observations on soil minerals emphasize several important features of mineral nutrition. Most plants are specially adapted to more or less specific soil types. These soils possess a *suitable concentration* of the minerals which that species particularly needs; too much may have toxic effects, too little may result in poor growth. A second point is that the correct *ion balance* must exist in the soil. Lack of one element may result in another element, normally useful to the plant, acting in a toxic manner. This is illustrated by the fact that calcicoles may be unable to grow on calcium-deficient soils because too much potassium is absorbed. Similarly, the water cultures described below will grow plants well only if there is the correct physiological balance of nutrients.

Antagonism may occur between two similar ions. Such *ion competition* may take place if both ions are absorbed into the root cells by a similar carrier system; both ions appear to compete for the same site on the carrier. For instance, the presence of potassium antagonizes magnesium uptake, while uptake of rubidium or calcium affects potassium uptake, although, perhaps surprisingly, sodium does not interfere with potassium and must presumably be taken up through a different carrier system.

The study of the soil and the minerals it contains is a vital part of the investigation of plant mineral nutrition; on the other hand, it is equally important to know which minerals are taken up and how they are utilized in plant metabolism before conclusions can be drawn regarding the economic and effective use of fertilizers and soil improvement techniques.

5.2 The mineral requirement

In addition to the elements carbon, hydrogen and oxygen that may be absorbed as water, carbon dioxide or oxygen, and which together make up a large part of the weight of a plant, there are a large number of mineral elements which are as necessary for plant growth. This necessity for various mineral elements has been investigated by the use of water cultures. A complete nutrient medium can be made up containing all the minerals that are thought to be necessary, and then separate media are made up omitting one nutrient mineral in each case (see Appendix, p. 186). The growth of young barley plants in different culture solutions is illustrated in fig. 5.1.

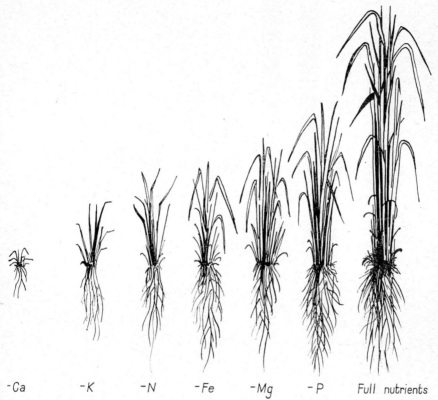

-Ca   -K   -N   -Fe   -Mg   -P   Full nutrients

FIG. 5.1. The nutrients required by barley (*Hordeum* sp.). The plant on the right was provided with all the minerals essential for plant growth. The remainder had similar nutrients except that the mineral indicated was omitted from the culture solution.

Calcium, potassium, nitrogen and iron are particularly important in the growth of barley. The presence and amounts of the various minerals actually metabolized can be found by drying, washing and subsequent analysis. Fig. 5.2 illustrates the amounts of these minerals in young plants of winter wheat; again nitrogen and potassium are particularly important.

Experiments on the mineral requirements of lower organisms such as fungi and bacteria are similar in principle and are particularly useful, as these organisms have a quick growth (or reproductive) rate. Sterile agar is

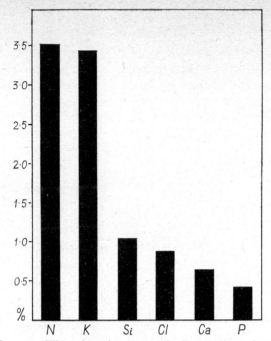

Fig. 5.2. The mineral content of winter wheat plants.

Relative amounts of various minerals in young winter wheat plants sampled in April, expressed as per cent of total dry matter.

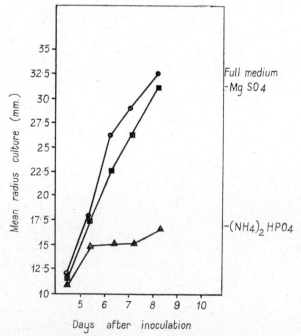

Fig. 5.3. Growth of *Mucor* with the mineral nutrients indicated omitted from the culture medium. (Class result.)

used as the medium for growth, and the organisms are grown in flat Petri dishes. (The preparation of the nutrient media is described in the Appendix on p. 187.) If the fungus *Mucor* is grown on a series of different nutrient media the effect on the growth rate is very marked; phosphate and ammonium ions are particularly useful for this species (see fig. 5.3).

Techniques of this sort have shown that there are six essential *major elements* which are required in fairly large quantities (see p. 88). These are nitrogen, potassium, calcium, phosphorus, magnesium and sulphur. Seven

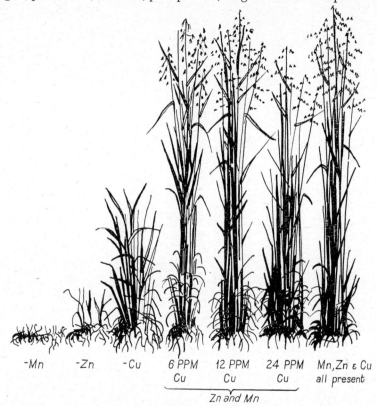

-Mn	-Zn	-Cu	6 PPM Cu	12 PPM Cu	24 PPM Cu	Mn,Zn & Cu all present

Zn and Mn

FIG. 5.4. Some minor nutrients essential for plant growth (oats). The plant on the right was provided with all the minerals essential for plant growth. The three on the left had similar nutrients but lacked the one indicated. The remaining plants had a full medium, but with different concentrations of copper. Note that there is an *optimum concentration* for copper; too much has a mildly detrimental effect.

further *minor elements* may also be classified as essential. Iron, chlorine, copper, manganese, zinc, molybdenum and boron are of certain importance, though they are required only in small quantities, often only a few parts per million (see fig. 5.4 and Appendix, p. 188). A few other minor nutrients, for instance, fluorine, cobalt and nickel, may also be of some importance.

A Summary of Minerals used by Plants.

Element	Form in which absorbed	Quantity utilized (approx.) as per cent of dry wt of plant	Functions	Effect of deficiency	Ecological and agricultural notes	Fertilizers
MAJOR ELEMENTS						
1 Nitrogen	NO_3^- (or NH_4^+)	3·5	Amino-acids, proteins and nucleotides	Chlorosis, small-sized plants	Frequently deficient; organic manuring and addition of nitrogenous fertilizers often necessary	Ammonium sulphate, sodium nitrate, nitro-chalk (ammonium nitrate and fine chalk)
2 Potassium	K^+	3·4	Enzyme, amino-acid and protein synthesis. Cell membranes. Increases vigour	Leaves have yellow edges; premature death	Plants need more potassium after heavy manuring with nitrogen and phosphorus. Most available on acid soils, though it may be leached out	Potassium sulphate
3 Calcium	Ca^{++}	0·7	Calcium pectate of cell-walls. Development of stem and root apices	Stunting of the root and stem	Little present in acid soils. Has important effect on soil by assisting flocculation of clay particles	Nitro-chalk, calcium phosphate, basic slag, superphosphate of lime [$Ca(H_2PO_4)_2 + CaSO_4$]
4 Phosphorus	$H_3PO_4^-$ (orthophosphate)	0·4	Formation of 'high-energy phosphate' (ATP and ADP). Nucleic acids. Phosphorylation of sugars	Small-sized plants; leaves a dull, dark green	Frequently deficient. Little is available over pH 7	Superphosphate of lime, calcium phosphate, basic slag
5 Magnesium	Mg^{++}	Small quantity	Part of the chlorophyll molecule. Activator of some of the enzymes in phosphate metabolism	Chlorosis; older leaves turn yellow, their veins remain green	Often deficient on acid soils	Magnesium sulphate, basic slag
6 Sulphur	$SO_4^=$	Small quantity	Proteins which contain thiol (-SH) groups	Chlorosis	Seldom deficient in Great Britain due to sulphuric acid contained in atmospheric pollution	—
MINOR ELEMENTS						
7 Iron	Fe^{++}	Small quantity	Chlorophyll synthesis. Cytochromes	Chlorosis, young leaves turn yellow-	Much less available on calcareous soils, being in the form	Chelated iron (in which the iron is bonded to an organic

thesis in the reactions in which oxygen is produced

No.	Element	Ion	Amount	Function	Deficiency symptoms	Remarks
9	Copper	Cu^{++}	Trace (less than 0·0001 per cent)	Activator group of polyphenol and ascorbic oxidase enzyme systems	Dieback of shoots	Helps to improve soil condition
10	Manganese	Mn^{++}	,,	Activator of some enzymes (e.g. carboxylases)	Chlorosis and grey-specks on leaves	Manganese is in the divalent state in acid soils and is readily available even to a toxic level. At high pH manganese is in the trivalent state, which plants cannot utilize
11	Zinc	Zn^{++}	,,	,,	Leaf malformation	More often deficient on acid soils due to adsorption on to colloidal complexes in soil
12	Molybdenum	Mo^{+++} or $^{++++}$	,,	Nitrogen metabolism, nitrate reductase enzyme	Size of plants slightly reduced	If molybdenum is deficient plants may survive if nitrogen is supplied as NH_4^+, but not if supplied as NO_3^-
13	Boron	$BO_3^{\equiv}$ or $B_4O_7^{=}$ (borate or tetraborate)	Trace	Influences Ca^{++} uptake and utilization. Differentiation and pollen germination	Brown heart disease	Easily leached from soils, particularly those of low pH
14	Cobalt	Co^{++}	,,	Various roles in symbiotic nitrogen-fixing plants	—	—
15	Fluorine, nickel	F^- Ni^{++}	,,	Not known, but possibly essential in some cases	—	—

NON-ESSENTIAL ELEMENTS

No.	Element	Ion	Amount	Function	Deficiency symptoms	Remarks
16	Silicon	$H_2SiO_4^{=}$	1·0 (grasses)	Straw formation (calcium silicates). Not essential to most plants	Slight decrease in weight	—
17	Sodium	Na^+	Trace	Osmotic and anion/cation balance, probably not essential to most plants	Effects slight	—
18	Aluminium	Al^{+++}	,,	Not essential. May cause upset to cell division system	—	More available in acid soils; it may prevent the growth of calcicoles

Sodium is frequently absorbed by plants, but is not essential (except in halophytes), though its presence is sometimes regarded as beneficial. Silicon is absorbed by grasses in some quantity, but most of these seem to be able to live healthily without it. Aluminium is also frequently absorbed, sometimes with toxic results, causing upsets to the cell-division system, at other times causing no apparent damage.

The table above summarizes the importance of the various minerals utilised by plants.

5.3 Uptake of minerals

There are four main stages in mineral uptake. First, that in which mineral ions diffuse from the soil solution into the inter-cellular spaces of the root apex. In the second stage ions may become adsorbed on to the cell walls, and in the third stage may diffuse through the cell wall and outer cytoplasmic membrane (plasma membrane) into the cytoplasm. Finally, if

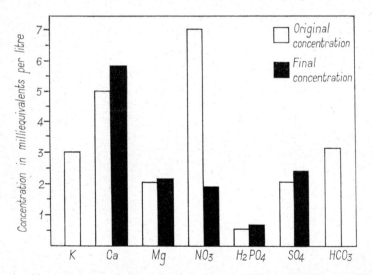

FIG. 5.5. Changes in concentration of nutrient solution due to uptake of water and ions by barley plants. (After Brierley (1958). An Approach to the Teaching of Salt Uptake in Plants. *School Science Review*, No. 138, p. 254.)

the plant is somewhat starved of minerals these ions may accumulate in the vacuole of that cell, but, on the other hand, if the vacuole already contains a high concentration of ions, then they may be transferred to the cytoplasm of the next cell directly, probably through the cell–cell protoplasmic connections, the plasmodesmata (see fig. 6.8).

The uptake of minerals into both cytoplasm and vacuoles is probably best investigated in the first instance, by extending the culture solution experiments described above so that changes in external nutrient concentration are noted. It is found that the concentrations of many of the minerals are radically changed during the course of the experiment; fig. 5.5 illustrates this with barley. Potassium ions are entirely absorbed, nitrate is also strongly absorbed and other elements relatively less. Clearly some minerals are taken up more readily than others; the problem is, how are they absorbed and why are some selectively absorbed in preference to others?

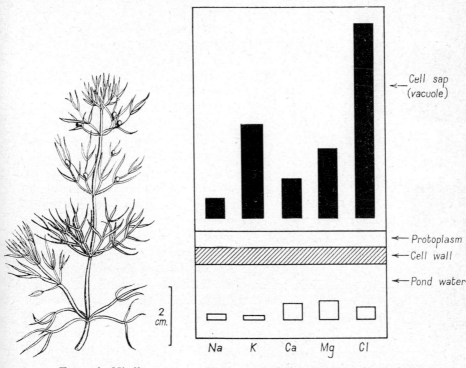

FIG. 5.6. *Nitella.*

A coenocytic alga useful in investigation of the concentration of ions in the vacuole.

FIG. 5.7. Relative concentrations of different ions in pond water and the vacuolar sap of *Nitella.* (After Brierley (1958). An Approach to the Teaching of Salt Uptake in Plants. *School Science Review,* No. 138, p. 254.)

The next step is to determine the internal and external concentrations of ions to find out the magnitude of any concentration difference, as it may be difficult for ions to diffuse into a vacuole which already contains more dissolved material than the external solution. Work with the large fresh-water algae *Valonia* and *Nitella* (see fig. 5.6) has proved to be particularly useful, as their cell sap is easily extracted and the internal concentration can be compared with that of the pond water in which they were growing (see fig.

G

5.7). In this species it is clear that sodium, potassium, calcium, magnesium and chloride ions are all at a much higher concentration in the vacuole than in the pond water, but again all the ions are not absorbed to the same extent. These results emphasize two important features of mineral uptake: first that the cytoplasmic membrane has some system by which ions are selectively absorbed, and secondly, that if this diffusion against a concentration gradient is to take place, then some energy will be required to drive the ions into the stronger internal solution of the vacuole. Similar results have been obtained with higher plants using the sap collected from cut surfaces and by rapid freezing techniques, the concentration differences being even more marked.

It used to be thought that the principal sources of this energy came from the thermal energy of the ions themselves and that once the ions reached the vacuole they were adsorbed and in some way taken out of free solution, thus lowering the internal concentration and allowing more ions to enter. However, experiments on the conductivity of the cell sap of algal coenocytes have indicated that the ions are in free solution and in no way adsorbed. Another indication that the ions are in free solution is that the osmotic pressure of the sap rises after a period of salt uptake.

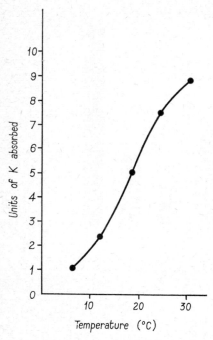

FIG. 5.8. Effect of temperature on the absorption of potassium by excised barley roots. (After Brierley (1958). An Approach to the Teaching of Salt Uptake in Plants. *School Science Review*, No. 138, p. 254.)

Mineral uptake is a characteristic of actively metabolizing tissues; this suggests that the energy required to drive the ions into the vacuole comes from some active metabolic process such as respiration. This suggestion is supported by an experiment in which the absorption of potassium by young barley root tips is related to temperature (see fig. 5.8). This type of curve is typical for enzyme-controlled processes such as respiration, in which the rate of the reaction about doubles itself for a rise in temperature of 10° C.; in other words, the Q_{10} is near 2. The rate of a physical process such as the diffusion of ions does not rise nearly so fast, the Q_{10} being about 1.3.

If respiration is involved, then the effect of oxygen on the rate of uptake should be marked. A simple experiment involves the uptake of bromide ions by young barley root tips in air and in nitrogen (for full details see Appendix, p. 189). If nitrogen is unavailable coal gas may be used, but this also acts as a respiratory inhibitor and is rather unsatisfactory. At the same time the temperature effect can be examined. Absorption of bromide in nitrogen is only about 10 per cent of that in air at room temperature; full results are given in the table below:

	Temperature (° C)	Uptake (expressed as a percentage of that in air)
Air	17	100
Nitrogen	17	10
Coal gas	17	8
Air	3	28

Table to show the absorption of bromide by barley root tips under different conditions (Class results.)

This experiment shows that aerobic respiration is a necessity for any reasonable uptake of ions such as bromide.

Further evidence of the close relationship between respiration and salt uptake comes from observations on the effect of adding a salt to a respiring tissue and estimating any changes in the respiratory rate. Very often a stimulation of the respiratory rate follows; this is known as the *salt respiration effect*. However, not all salts produce the effect; this is probably due to their specific effects on the absorbing system in the cytoplasm. Part A of the graph (fig. 5.9) illustrates the rate of respiration of the yeast-like fungus, *Torilopsis utilis*, when a salt is added. It must also be emphasized that the concentration of salt that has to be added to produce the salt respiration effect is much higher than would exist in the soil solution. In this species sodium has no effect, but ammonium phosphate causes a considerable stimulation. That the ammonium phosphate is absorbed by the fungus and at the same time removed from the solution is shown by separate estimation (see Appendix, p. 190), the results of which are shown in parts C and B of the graph, fig. 5.9.

The connection of salt uptake with respiration can be further investigated by the use of inhibitors. For instance, $M/1,000$ potassium cyanide, which inhibits the terminal oxidase systems with copper and iron activator groups, also has a considerable effect on the rate of salt uptake.

Finally, some evidence relating to the means of uptake has come from experiments using radioactive ions which can be traced. This technique is particularly useful, as the intact plant may be used. Tracer rubidium, which is taken up in much the same way as potassium, has been found to enter the cytoplasm readily by diffusion, but the ions are passed only relatively slowly into the vacuole. In addition, ions quite often come out of the cytoplasm while more of the same sort are still entering. It seems that the cytoplasm–vacuole membrane or tonoplast is the zone which is only passed with difficulty and the expenditure of energy: entry into the

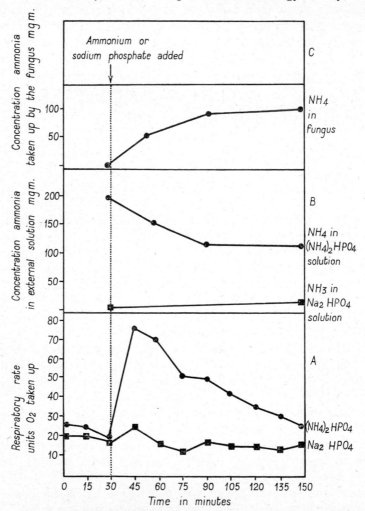

FIG. 5.9. Salt respiration and the absorption of ammonium and sodium ions (see p. 93).

cytoplasm, through the plasma membrane, from the external solution is relatively easy.

We can conclude that some process coupled with the respiratory system is responsible for driving ions across the tonoplast and into the vacuole. It is possible that a carrier is produced in the cytoplasm which is able to pick up the ion which has diffused into the cytoplasm and transfer it to the tonoplast in such a way that it is released into the vacuole. The formation and possibly the regeneration of the carrier is probably the step at which the process is linked with the respiratory system. The differential accumulation of ions in the vacuole suggests that there must be more than one carrier involved. Although no carrier has ever been positively identified, it is likely that there is at least one carrier for anions and one for cations.

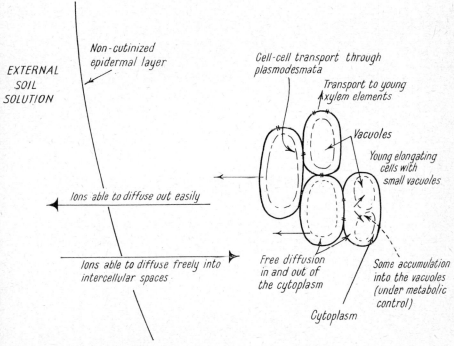

FIG. 5.10. The uptake of mineral ions into the cells behind the root apex.

It has been suggested that the production and regeneration of the carriers is connected to the redox systems of respiration, but the matter is still anything but clear, and at the moment there is no complete answer to the mechanism by which mineral ions are accumulated in plants. The process of mineral uptake is summarized in fig. 5.10.

5.4 Mineral transport

Once the ions have been absorbed from the soil solution they may pass into the intercellular spaces, cell walls, cytoplasm or vacuoles of the cells behind the root apex. How then are they transported to areas where they are required? The first phase of this transport must end at the xylem. Although some movement of ions takes place through the apoplast (see p. 28), much of the transport may occur through the living system of the *symplast*.

If the plant is well supplied with minerals this takes place from the cytoplasm of one cell direct to the cytoplasm of another, through the plasmodesmata, without many of the ions being temporarily accumulated in the intervening

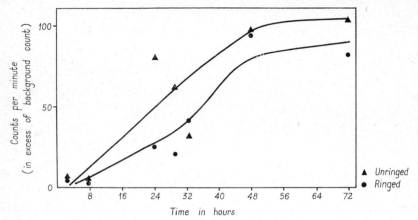

FIG. 5.11. Accumulation of P^{32} by ringed and unringed plants of *Skimmia*. (Class results.)

vacuoles. Most of the ions are transported in the form in which they are absorbed, but nitrogen is transported as nitrate by herbs, and as amides by trees.

Once the ions reach the xylem they are drawn upwards in the xylem

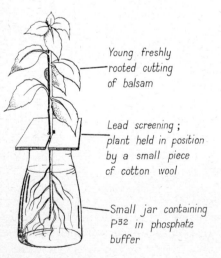

Young freshly rooted cutting of balsam

Lead screening; plant held in position by a small piece of cotton wool

Small jar containing P^{32} in phosphate buffer

FIG. 5.12. Apparatus used for investigating the absorption of P^{32} by young plants of balsam (*Impatiens sultani*).

stream. That it is the xylem and not the phloem that is principally important for this upwards movement can be shown by ringing experiments, in which the phloem elements are removed. This can be demonstrated most effectively by placing two similar plants of *Skimmia* or other woody plants in a solution containing radioactive phosphorous, P^{32}, after one plant has had its stem ringed. The counts per minute near the apex of each plant are measured with a Geiger counter until sufficient tracer has accumulated (see fig. 5.11). After about three days both plants are removed from the solution and their aerial parts placed for about two weeks against a photographic plate. After development it is seen that both autoradiographs show tracer in their aerial parts. However, phloem transport also takes place, especially in tissues where the transpiration stream is low, such as the apical meristems; these are also tissues in which metabolism of the minerals is vitally important. That lateral diffusion from the xylem to the phloem normally takes place is well shown by another tracer experiment involving the use of radioactive phosphorus (for full details of the use of radioactive tracers see Appendix, p. 193). A small shrub such as a willow with three shoots is allowed to grow in a solution containing radioactive phosphorus. One shoot is left intact as a control; in the second the xylem and phloem are separated by a piece of thick waxed paper and then bound together; in the third the xylem and phloem are separated and then rejoined, without the waxed paper, as another control. After about twenty-four hours the treated segments are sampled, sectioned lengthways and the flat surfaces placed on photo-

FIG. 5.13. Autoradiograph showing P^{32} accumulation by balsam (*Impatiens sultani*).

An intact, rooted cutting was placed for two days in a solution containing six microcuries of P^{32}. The roots were then removed and the autoradiograph obtained by placing a photographic plate over the flattened plant. Tracer has accumulated throughout the leaves, though most strongly in the veins.

graphic plates. The resulting autoradiographs show that in the first and last segments the tracer is uniformly distributed in both xylem and phloem, but in the second very little has passed into the phloem. This indicates that although the xylem is the main path of transport of ions, lateral diffusion into the phloem does take place to a considerable extent.

The leaf petiole is a structure which has also been investigated with reference to the transport of mineral and organic molecules. Hot wax and heat jackets surrounding the petioles, causing coagulation of the protoplasm of the living phloem elements, have been found to prevent the downwards transport of organic molecules from the leaf but to leave the uptake of minerals into the leaf unaffected. This has been shown using radio-active phosphorus, P^{32}, its presence in the leaf being identified auto-radiographically or with a counter.

Although it looks as though the xylem is usually the most important route for the upwards transport of mineral ions, there is some evidence, obtained from ringing experiments, that the phloem is of comparatively greater importance in this role in woody plants. Ringing experiments on trees have been shown to have a marked effect on the upward transport of amides.

Once the mineral ions reach the leaf and aerial parts of the plant they diffuse out of the finest xylem elements and are finally absorbed in the cells, where they are required for their various metabolic roles. Studies of auto-radiographs of plants that have been growing in various tracer elements show to some extent how the ions are utilized, and can be a great help in understanding the mineral nutrition of plants. Balsam (*Impatiens sultani*) provides useful material (see figs. 5.12 and 5.13), as uptake is particularly rapid, phosphate being distributed throughout the leaves, after an initial accumulation in the growing apices.

5.5   Metabolic utilization of mineral ions

Once the minerals are in the xylem they are transported in the transpiration stream to the stems and leaves. In the young stem apices rapid

$$NO_3^- \longrightarrow NH_4^+$$

nitrate
reductase
(Mo ions needed)

+

$$
\begin{array}{l}
COOH \\
| \\
CH_2 \\
| \\
CH_2 \\
| \\
CO \\
| \\
COOH
\end{array}
$$
α-ketoglutaric acid

$$
\begin{array}{l}
COOH \\
| \\
CH_2 \\
| \\
CH_2 \\
| \\
CH.NH_2 \\
| \\
COOH
\end{array}
$$
glutamic acid

growth is taking place and active transport of the ions may be carried out so that these minerals can be incorporated into the various substances and structures being laid down. Nitrogen, arriving as nitrate, is metabolized into amino-acids and proteins. The enzyme nitrate reductase (which requires molybdenum as its activator group) reduces the nitrate to ammonium ions. These cause the amination of the Citric Acid Cycle intermediates, such as α-ketoglutaric acid to form glutamic acid.

Phosphate ions may exist free in the cytoplasm for any length of time and are continually being used and reformed through the various phosphorylation reactions. Considerable quantities of phosphate are continually required for the various photosynthetic and respiratory intermediates as well as for the formation of the high-energy phosphates (ATP and ADP). It is possible to distinguish those ions which have a structural or metabolic role: particularly nitrate, phosphate, calcium and sulphate. Other ions, such as magnesium, iron and copper, are vital as parts of enzymes or catalysts and are called *catalytic ions*. The division of mineral ions into these groups bears a relationship to the quantities of minerals that are required. Those with a catalytic role are needed in only small quantities compared with those concerned in the production of structural or metabolic substances.

5.6 The nitrogen cycle

It is probably a mistake to suggest that one element is more important in plant metabolism than another, as varying quantities of all the minerals mentioned above are essential to plant growth. However, the turnover of nitrogen in plants and in the soil is rightly regarded as one of the most important aspects of mineral nutrition.

Relatively few plants are able to utilize atmospheric nitrogen direct (see nitrogen-fixing organisms, below), but are dependent on nitrate for most of their nitrogen requirements, although ammonia is also absorbed. Many soils contain some inorganic nitrogen compounds derived from fertilizers and from the decay of plant and animal materials. Saprophytic bacteria, such as *Bacillus megatherium*, and various species of fungi, are mainly responsible for the final breakdown of dead organic material resulting in the release of ammonia into the soil solution. The activities of saprophytic fungi are particularly noticeable in woodland. In beechwoods in the autumn there are to be found a wide selection of fruiting-bodies of litter-decomposing species, such as the yellow-staining mushroom (*Agaricus xanthoderma*), the small purple-pink *Mycena pura* and the brown *Marasmius peronatus*. Wood-decomposing species that are common include the bracket fungi, *Polystictus versicolor* and *Trametes rubescens*.

Although large quantities of ammonia are toxic to plant life, several species of bacteria that are common in soils are able to oxidize ammonia.

The chemosynthetic nitrifying bacteria *Nitrosomonas* and *Nitrococcus* oxidize the ammonia to nitrite to release energy which they utilize for carbohydrate synthesis:

$$2NH_3^+ + 3O_2 \longrightarrow 2NO_2^- + 2H^+ + 2H_2O$$

Another common chemosynthesitic bacterium, *Nitrobacter*, oxidizes the nitrite to form nitrate, again with the release of energy which is utilized by the bacteria:

$$2NO_2^- + O_2 \longrightarrow 2NO_3^-$$

The nitrate ions so formed are easily absorbed by plants. Although these equations are probably over-simplifications, they are useful in showing how chemosynthetic organisms may obtain their energy.

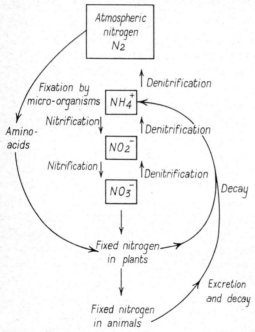

Another effect which is important in adding to the level of nitrogen compounds in the soil is the formation of nitric oxide and ammonia by high-tension discharges in the atmosphere; these substances dissolve easily in the rain. The nitrogen-fixing micro-organisms are, however, the chief means by which the level of fixed nitrogen in the soil is maintained. It is of interest that the fixation of atmospheric nitrogen by living things seems to be confined to micro-organisms; many examples have been listed of bacteria, algae and fungi being able to fix nitrogen, but so far there is no evidence that the higher plants, on their own, are able to carry out the process. On the other hand, lower organisms in a symbiotic association with other plants are frequently able to fix atmospheric nitrogen, even though both micro-organism and higher plant, when on their own, are usually unable to do so.

Unfortunately several other species of bacteria (e.g. *Micrococcus denitrificans*) are harmful, for they are able to reverse the processes of nitrogen fixation and nitrification. Fortunately they work effectively only in badly drained, oxygen-deficient soils.

The turnover of fixed nitrogen in living things and the soil is vitally necessary to most organisms; the relationships between nitrogen in the atmosphere, in the soil and in living things can be summarized in the nitrogen cycle.

5.7 Nitrogen-fixing organisms

Much difficulty has been experienced in the past in determining the ability of organisms to fix nitrogen. There are several reasons for this; one is that some organisms may show an apparent growth without the synthesis of any new protoplasmic material, in other cases organisms have been able to obtain fixed nitrogen from the small amounts of the oxides of nitrogen existing in the atmosphere. In addition, contamination of cultures has sometimes caused confusion as another organism may be responsible for the fixation. Finally, difficulties have been experienced in the analysis of nitrogen actually fixed, and in the preparation of nitrogen-free culture media. The most useful technique for the analysis of fixed nitrogen is the micro-Kjeldahl method (described on p. 191, in the Appendix), but recently useful results have been obtained with N^{15} tracer nitrogen, which can be analysed using a mass-spectrometer.

Fixation of nitrogen is a surprisingly frequent feature of free-living lower organisms. It is found in some species of saprophytic soil bacteria, photosynthetic bacteria, chemosynthetic bacteria, blue-green algae and fungi. Of the bacteria the three genera *Clostridium*, *Azotobacter* and *Beijerinckia* contain species that are nitrogen fixing. All these genera are widespread and common; *Clostridium* is particularly interesting, as it is an obligate anaerobe. The other two genera are aerobic, but *Azotobacter* tends to live in less-acid soils than *Beijerinckia*. Several photosynthetic bacteria are nitrogen fixing, but *Rhodospirillum rubrum* is of special interest, as fixation actually appears to be associated with the photosynthetic process. *Desulphovibrio* is an economically important chemosynthetic and obligately anaerobic organism that is also nitrogen fixing. About twenty species of blue-green algae are known to be nitrogen fixing. Many of these occur free in the soil and in ponds and streams, but they are also commonly found in symbiotic associations: *Nostoc* and *Anabaena* are well-known examples. Few fungi appear to be nitrogen fixing, with the exception of some saprophytic yeasts that are found in heathland soils.

Fixation of nitrogen by symbiotic association is of particular biological interest, and includes the well-known examples of fixation in the root nodules of leguminous plants. Under normal conditions bacteria of the genus *Rhizobium*, which on their own are unable to fix atmospheric nitrogen, infect the root hairs of young leguminous plants and cause the formation of nodules. The bacteria stimulate meristematic activity in the outer cortex of the host and a nodule begins its development. Differentiation from the apex of the nodule (see fig. 5.14) results in the formation of several distinct

zones. First, there is the uninfected apical meristem itself, then a zone
of newly infected tissue followed by a large area of dense, active bacterial
tissue and finally a zone of tissue disintegration. At the same time
the apex forms a cortex, endodermis and vascular strand surrounding
the central bacterial tissue and allowing for its protection and nourish-
ment. The degree of infection is very varied (see fig. 5.14) and depends
on several factors, such as the genetic constitution of the host legume,
availability of minerals such as boron in the soil and the actual age of

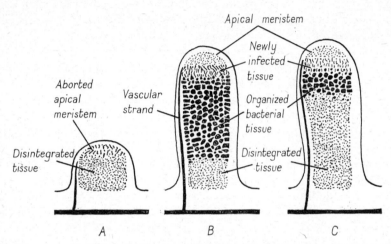

FIG. 5.14. Sections of effective and ineffective root nodules of clover.
    A. Ineffective nodule with aborted meristem.
    B. Healthy effective nodule.
    C. Ineffective nodule with too rapid disintegration.
(After Brierley (1957). Plant Symbiosis. *School Science Review*, No. 136, p. 360.)

the nodule itself. As the nodule develops, the bacteria multiply, utilizing
carbohydrates produced by the host, and the nodule becomes effective and
the bacteria nitrogen fixing. At this time the nodule may appear pink due
to the formation of haemoglobin and it is now known that the haemoglobin
has an important function in the fixation system. Ultimately the bacteria
at the base of the nodule attack the host tissues and disintegration results.
In some cases the genetic constitution of the host and unfavourable soil
conditions may result in the apical meristem not functioning properly or,
on the other hand, the rate of disintegration of the tissues may be too fast
and very little fixation may take place. The factors governing the formation
of healthy and effective nodules are therefore very specific and carefully
balanced between host and bacterium.
    Nitrogen fixation by symbiotic organisms in association with plants is
by no means confined to leguminous plants, and is probably a very much

wider phenomenon than is generally realized. The lichens are well-known examples of symbiotic organisms, part fungus and part alga. Recent research has indicated that in some species, such as *Peltigera praetextata*, in which the algal partner is *Nostoc*, there is a significant transference of fixed nitrogen from the blue-green alga to the fungus. It has also shown that many lichens also contain bacteria of the genus *Azotobacter*, but here there is no conclusive evidence that any nitrogen fixed by the bacteria contributes significantly to the overall level of fixed nitrogen in the lichen. The thalloid liverwort *Blasia pusilla* is another organism which contains colonies of *Nostoc*; these are easily seen as small, dark, hollow spots on the lower surface of the thallus. Among the ferns, *Azolla filiculoides*, a small fern found occasionally in southern England floating in ditches and ponds, has also been shown to be symbiotic with the blue-green alga *Anabaena*; as a result the fern is possibly able to live in water deficient of fixed nitrogen.

In higher plants the association of the alder *Alnus glutinosa* with an actinomycete, a small filamentous organism having some affinities with the bacteria, results in the formation of root nodules in which nitrogen fixation takes place. Experiments using the heavy N^{15} isotope of nitrogen have indicated convincingly that the nitrogen fixed in the nodules is made available to the whole plant. Just as in the *Rhizobium*–legume relationship, there is evidence that neither the alder nor the actinomycete are able, on their own, to fix nitrogen. The effect of the presence of nodules when the alder is growing on a medium not containing fixed nitrogen is shown in fig. 5.15, on the other hand, if the alder is supplied with fixed nitrogen in the form of nitrate, then the presence or absence of nodules makes little difference to the growth that takes place (see fig. 5.16).

There are numerous other examples of reported and confirmed symbiotic and nitrogen-fixing associations of higher plants with micro-organisms, and it seems likely that such relationships are surprisingly widespread, contributing to a very real extent to the amount of fixed nitrogen available to plants and the fertility of the soil.

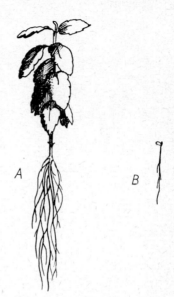

FIG. 5.15. Alder (*Alnus gluti-nosa*).

Growth of nodulated and un-nodulated plants. Grown for 30 weeks in solution without fixed nitrogen.

A. Plant with nodules.
B. Plant without nodules.

Fig. 5.16.
Alder (*Alnus glutinosa*).

Growth of nodulated and un-nodulated plants.

A. Nodulated plant grown for 21 weeks in solution containing no nitrate.

B. Un-nodulated plant grown for the same time in solution containing nitrate.

5.8 The mechanism of nitrogen fixation

The use of N^{15} has been very useful for research on the mechanism of the fixation process. The most conclusive work, done by Professor P. W. Wilson in America, has been carried out mainly using *Azotobacter* cultures. In one set of experiments it was established that if *Azotobacter* cultures were placed in gaseous N^{15}, then the isotope was rapidly accumulated by the bacteria. In another set of experiments *Azotobacter* was placed in ordinary gaseous nitrogen, but the bacteria were supplied with ammonia labelled with N^{15}. Under these conditions *Azotobacter* utilized the ammonia rather than the gaseous source. In both experiments the labelled nitrogen was found in the simple amino-acid glutamic acid. This suggested that *Azotobacter* takes up atmospheric nitrogen and uses it to form ammonia. The conditions inside the root nodule are thought to be relatively anaerobic and this assists the reduction process in leguminous plants. The role of haemoglobin in the nodule seems to be in the early stages of capture of molecular nitrogen. It is known that nitrogen can oxidize haemoglobin which can in turn be reduced by the enzyme system of the *Rhizobium*. Although the method of ammonia formation is still not clear, the enzyme *nitrogenase* which is responsible for this first stage of the fixation process has been partially characterized. There is more evidence on the formation of glutamic acid. α-ketoglutaric acid is a Citric Acid Cycle intermediate (see p. 71), and the ammonia combines with this acid to form glutamic acid (see p. 98).

A final difficulty is how does the fixed nitrogen, now in the form of amino-acids, find its way out into the soil again? It is almost certain that both the legumes and the free-living bacteria secrete reasonable quantities of nitrogenous substances into the soil. The most likely suggestion is that they are secreted in the form of amino-acids and these are readily absorbed by plant roots.

5.9 Some agricultural and horticultural aspects of mineral nutrition

The study of mineral nutrition is obviously of vital importance in agriculture, where crop yields may be considerably increased by mineral addition. This is not always so easy as it may seem. The ideal method for adding minerals is still thought to be by organic manuring, as this provides the plants with a more or less balanced mineral supplement, as well as humus, which will help in the formation of a good soil structure. Unfortunately organic manures are expensive, and often hard to obtain in sufficient quantity, and so inorganic nutrients are nowadays used more frequently. There are several difficulties in the use of these substances. In the first place many of the minor nutrients, being required only in terms of a few parts per million, can easily be provided at too high a concentration and reach a toxic level. Secondly, many (e.g. zinc) tend to become unavailable due to adsorption on to the soil colloids. Finally, if these substances are to be of any use they must be moderately soluble, and this implies that they may be leached or washed out of the soil and lost to the plant.

It is most necessary to add the correct type and quantity of fertilizer for the desired crop. Some plants have higher demands for some nutrients than others. In other cases, although a fertilizer may cause additional growth, this may not occur in the part of the plant that is to be harvested. This can occur in potatoes, which, if given too much nitrogen, make considerable leaf growth and less tubers than they would otherwise have produced. Such a procedure is clearly most uneconomic. Recently some new fertilizer techniques have been tried for the addition of minor nutrients, in particular spraying the leaves rather than the soil with the liquid nutrient. In many cases, provided the cuticle of the plant is not too thick, considerable absorption of the ions may take place. Such a technique, if successful, is clearly likely to be more economic than fertilizing the soil.

Another new technique involves the use of an organic *chelate* iron from which the metal can be absorbed by calcifuge plants even in the presence of calcium ions. This may be of considerable value to gardeners who wish to grow calcifuges such as *Camellia* and *Rhododendron* on soils of high pH, though this substance is also eventually washed out of the soil and periodic additions are needed.

Finally, it must be emphasized that if crops are to be grown economically to give maximum yield and gardeners are to be successful with their more difficult plants, it is first necessary to understand the particular requirements and preferences of the crop or plant. Secondly, it is necessary to have a knowledge of the mineral status of the soil so that any necessary modification of it may be carried out with the minimum of expense.

6   The Biochemistry of Cell Activities

6.1   Introduction

In the foregoing chapters some of the basic vital processes that go on both in the cell and the plant as a whole have been analysed for the most part as separate functions. In this chapter the intention is to try to indicate how the cell acts, at a biochemical level, as an organized entity. To do this we must consider the steps in metabolism which involve the role and reduplication of the nucleic acids, the synthesis of proteins and the working of enzymes, the formation and functions of the more complex carbohydrates and of the fats.

In this way, with the wealth of detail on the ultra-structure of the cell that is now available, we may gain a glimpse of the cell acting as a self-contained, organized whole, but even so, varying in its function within the limits imposed by its own genetic constitution and relative to its position in the scheme of organization of the plant as a whole.

6.2   The nucleic acids

Since the time of Morgan in the 1910s it has been firmly established that the chromosomes are the site of the hereditary genes, which are arranged in linear order along the chromosomes. In normal cytological preparations of dividing cells (metaphase mitosis) the chromosomes are clearly visible as double, rod-like structures (see fig. 6.1) due to the staining action of the aceto- or fuchsin stains being used (see Appendix, p. 194). These stains are specific for deoxyribose nucleic acid (DNA), while the ribonucleic acid (RNA) found in the microsomes, nucleolus and free in the cytoplasm remains unstained.

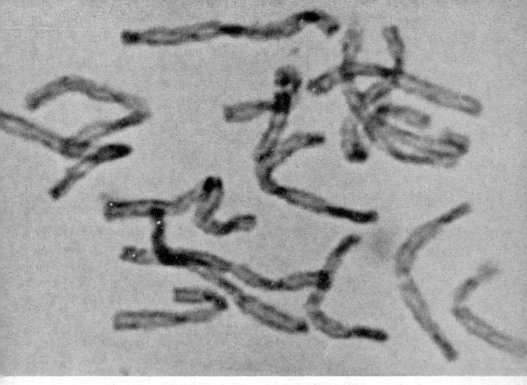

FIG. 6.1. Mitotic metaphase in the onion (*Allium cepa*.)
Note the short, double chromosomes. $2n = 16$. Aceto-lacmoid–orcein squash.

FIG. 6.2. Mitotic anaphase in the peony (*Paeonia* sp.)
Aceto-lacmoid–orcein squash.

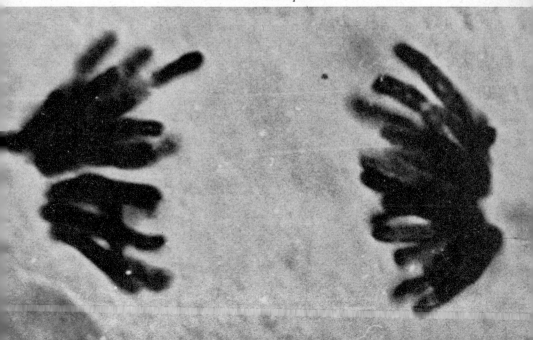

Replication of DNA

There is therefore good evidence that the genes of most organisms (with the possible exception of some of the viruses) are largely composed of DNA.

When mitosis takes place the chromosomes appear as short double strands, the double structure divides at the end of metaphase, and when the chromosomes are last clearly seen at anaphase or telophase (see fig. 6.2) they are single. The problem is, how does the chromosome with its protein core and DNA replicate itself during interphase before the chromosomes appear at the next division.

The answer lies in the unique structure of the DNA molecule. Classical work by Watson and Crick published in 1953 using X-ray-diffraction analysis techniques revealed that DNA is a long complex double helix (see fig. 6.3). Essentially each chain of the helix is composed of deoxyribose sugar molecules joined to one another by phosphate groups. In addition, each sugar molecule has attached a purine or pyrimidine base. This forms a nucleotide chain.

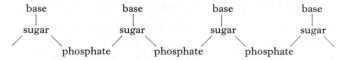

Finally, the two chains are kept together by hydrogen bonding between opposite bases. In DNA only four bases are found, adenine and thymine, guanine and cytosine. Hydrogen bonding is only possible between the pairs as given, *not*, for instance, between thymine and guanine. The bases can be arranged in different orders, and a particular sequence or 'code' determines the action of a particular gene.

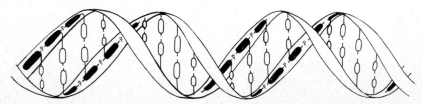

Fig. 6.3. The DNA molecule.

Each ribbon represents one nucleotide chain consisting of deoxyribose sugar joined by phosphate groups. The ribbons are held together by H-bonding between opposing bases.

Replication of a complex double helix of this sort, itself a molecular spiral within the visible spiralized chromosome itself (see fig. 6.4), must seem a considerable problem, but during resting stage, when the chromosome is in a long and relatively unspiralized state, the double helix separates into its two parent chains. This must itself require a progressive separation

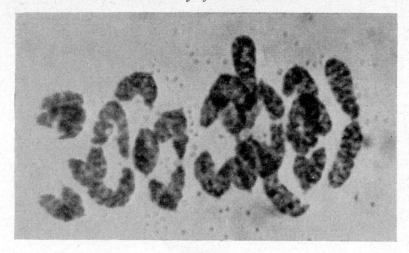

FIG. 6.4. Meiotic metaphase (first division) in the spiderwort (*Tradescantia virginiana*.)
Aceto-lacmoid–orcein squash showing spiralized chromosomes.

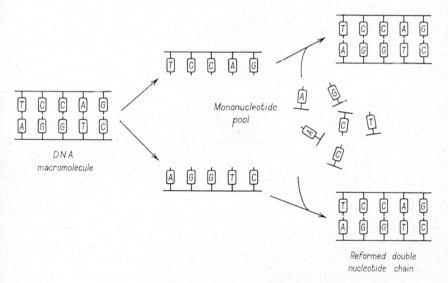

FIG. 6.5. Self-replication of the DNA molecule.

of the giant molecule of the double helix. As this is effected, then the bonds of the bases are left free for fresh mononucleotides to be attached. The nucleus contains a pool of these mononucleotides (see fig. 6.5), and as the correct, complementary, base is the only one capable of satisfying the particular spare bond, then a new nucleotide chain, identical to the original, is formed and replication is effected. As the mononucleotides are brought together, so coiling takes place and the original double helix is re-created (see fig. 6.6).

An interesting experiment has given support to the concept of a completely new DNA spiral being synthesized on to the template of the other in this manner. The chromosomes of the broad bean are particularly large and clear; if seedlings of the bean are grown in a medium containing the

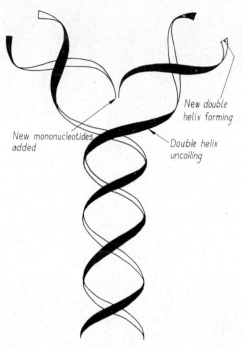

New double
helix forming

New mononucleotides
added

Double helix
uncoiling

FIG. 6.6. Unwinding and replication of the DNA molecule.

base thymidine labelled with tritium, then on examining the autoradiograph of root-tip metaphase chromosomes, these chromosomes are seen to be uniformly labelled. However, if the radioactive medium is then removed and the next division *but one* examined, then only *one* chromatid of each chromosome is labelled, the other chromatid, newly synthesized in the interphase from non-radioactive thymidine, does not expose the photographic emulsion (see fig. 6.7).

The arrangement of the paired bases along the DNA double helix not only allows for the replication of the DNA so that genetic information may be passed on through each cell division but it also provides a blueprint for the synthesis of RNA, a similar nucleic acid, containing ribose instead of deoxyribose sugar and also with the base *uracil* replacing thymine

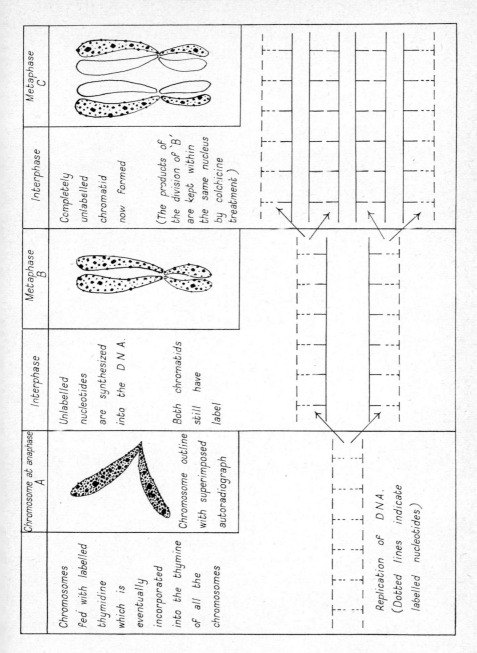

FIG. 6.7. The addition of labelled thymidine to dividing cells.

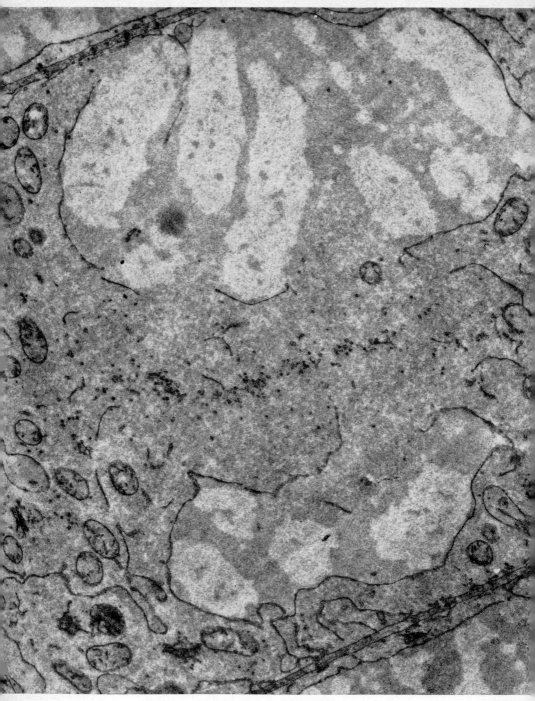

Fig. 6.8a. A telophase cell from the root apex of barley. (See fig 6.8b opposite.)

An electron-microscope photograph showing details of the newly divided cell. Note the two newly formed nuclei with their chromosome material still visible. The nuclear membrane has reformed except for occasional gaps. The mitochondria, cytoplasmic reticulum, ribosomes and *Golgi* body are clearly visible. Plasmodesmata are visible in the surrounding cell wall. (Courtesy of Dr. B. E. Juniper.)

The importance of RNA

Analysis of the RNA content of the cell has shown that it is found mainly in the *nucleolus*, the *ribosomes*, the *cytoplasmic* (or *endoplasmic*) *reticulum* and free in the cytoplasm. Electron-microscope photographs (see figs. 6.8 and 6.9) show that the reticulum is a plate-like, folded system,

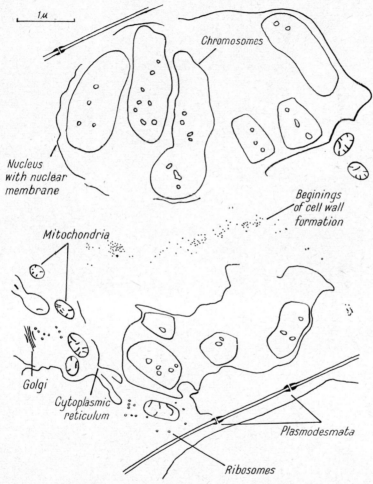

FIG. 6.8B. (See fig 6.8A opposite.)

widely dispersed through the cytoplasm. The ribosomes are minute rounded bodies which are usually more or less randomly distributed in young cells, though in older cells they may be associated with the reticulum. The *Golgi body* or *apparatus* (see figs. 1.1 and 6.8) appears to be a centre for the organization of the various membranes of the reticulum system. Much of the work carried out on the properties of the ribosomes and

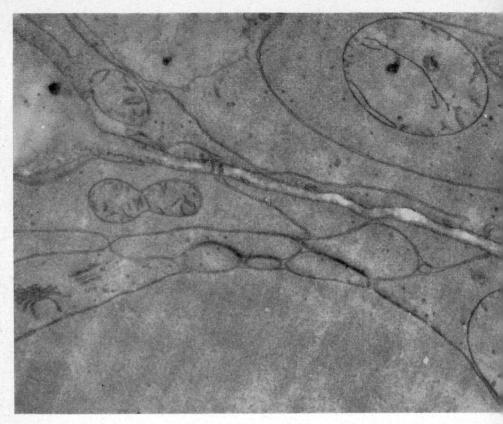

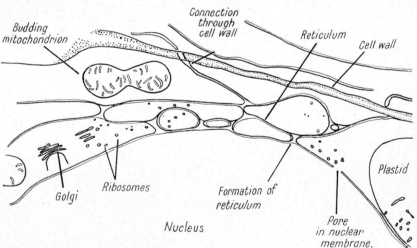

FIG. 6.9. Part of a cortical cell from the root of the broad bean (*Vicia faba*) showing the cytoplasmic reticulum; electron microscope photograph. (× 23,000.) (Courtesy of Dr. B. E. Juniper.)

reticulum have involved grinding and centrifuging techniques which have produced a mass of small articles, partly ribosomes and partly broken-up reticulum. These extracted particles are often given the name of *microsomes*.

Messenger or template RNA

The DNA template on the chromosome is the blueprint for the synthesis of the *messenger or template* RNA that is found on the ribosomes and possibly to some extent also on the reticulum. Recent electron-microscope photographs have shown that the reticulum frequently appears to connect up with the pores in the nuclear membrane (see fig. 6.9). There is a suggestion that this may be a visible sign of some RNA transference from the nucleus to the cytoplasmic organelles. The messenger RNA, organized on to the ribosomes, is the template for protein synthesis (see below and fig. 6.11).

Transfer RNA

The cytoplasmic RNA, called *transfer RNA*, consists of only a relatively small number of nucleotides (about eighty), and it is possibly synthesized from other RNA. Its function is also in protein synthesis, as it assists in the conveyance of amino-acids to the correct site on the messenger or template RNA (see fig. 6.12). How the forms of RNA and other substances cooperate in protein synthesis is described below (section 6.5).

Nucleolar RNA

The nucleolus has always been something of an enigma for the cytologist. Its disappearance during cell-division and reappearance during interphase suggested that it might be some sort of nucleic acid storage system, but at the present time there is no clear evidence as to the function of this organelle.

6.3 Synthesis of amino-acids and polypeptides

The amino-acids

The chromatograms obtained after algae had been photosynthesizing for some time in $C^{14}O_2$ (see p. 58) showed, in addition to the various carbohydrates, several labelled amino-acids. How these amino-acids came to be formed as indirect photosynthetic products is not entirely clear. On the other hand, use of N^{15} shows how some amino-acids are produced, for this tracer is rapidly accumulated into glutamic acid through the amination of α-ketoglutaric acid, an intermediate of the Citric Acid Cycle (see p. 98).

Although about sixty amino-acids have been identified in plant tissues, most cells contain fewer, and only about twenty are concerned in protein formation. Many, though not all, of these are formed from glutamic acid by *transamination* reactions. For instance, glutamic acid and oxaloacetic acid could combine to form α-ketoglutaric acid and aspartic acid:

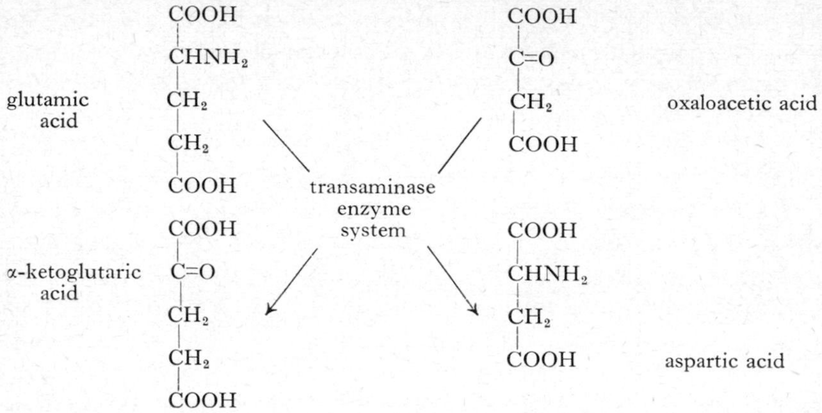

$$
\begin{array}{ll}
\text{glutamic} & \begin{array}{l} COOH \\ CHNH_2 \\ CH_2 \\ CH_2 \\ COOH \end{array}
\end{array}
\qquad
\begin{array}{l} COOH \\ C{=}O \\ CH_2 \\ COOH \end{array}
\quad \text{oxaloacetic acid}
$$

transaminase
enzyme
system

$$
\begin{array}{ll}
\text{α-ketoglutaric} \\ \text{acid} & \begin{array}{l} COOH \\ C{=}O \\ CH_2 \\ CH_2 \\ COOH \end{array}
\end{array}
\qquad
\begin{array}{l} COOH \\ CHNH_2 \\ CH_2 \\ COOH \end{array}
\quad \text{aspartic acid}
$$

Peptide bond formation

When several amino-acids are brought together on to the template RNA they join together by means of *peptide bonds*, to form proteins. The system by which two amino-acids join together to form a di-peptide is illustrated by the synthesis of glutamylcysteine.

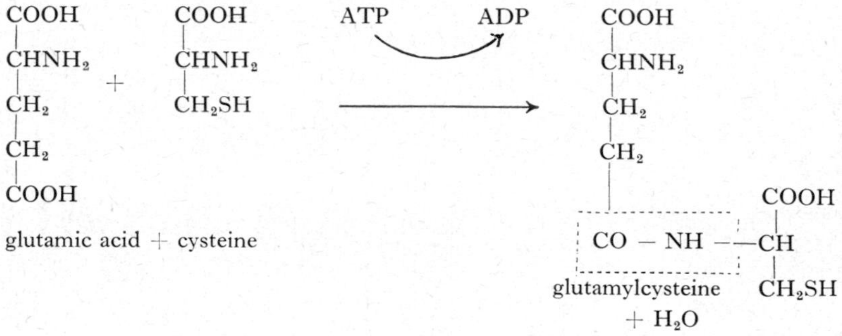

$$
\begin{array}{l} COOH \\ CHNH_2 \\ CH_2 \\ CH_2 \\ COOH \end{array}
\;+\;
\begin{array}{l} COOH \\ CHNH_2 \\ CH_2SH \end{array}
\qquad ATP \quad ADP \qquad
\begin{array}{l} COOH \\ CHNH_2 \\ CH_2 \\ CH_2 \\ \hline CO-NH \end{array}
\begin{array}{l} \\ \\ COOH \\ CH \\ CH_2SH \end{array}
$$

glutamic acid + cysteine

glutamylcysteine
+ H_2O

This condensation, in which the carboxyl group of the glutamic acid reacts with the amino-group of the cysteine, requires energy in the form of ATP. The tri-peptide glutathione is formed by a similar condensation reaction with glycine as the additional amino-acid. This energy-requiring, multiple condensation process by which amino-acids are joined together by peptide bonds to form polypeptides gives a repetitive structure of the following form, though the chain is a three-dimensional one with the amino-acids arranged at 120° to one another. R_1, R_2, R_3 represent these different amino-acids:

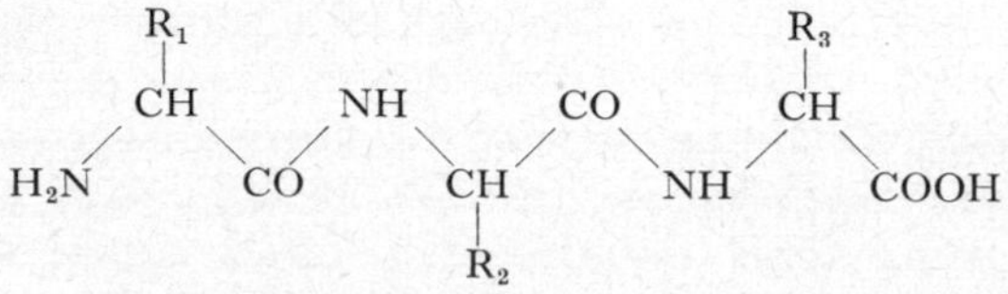

$$
H_2N \diagup \underset{\displaystyle R_1}{CH} \diagdown CO \diagup NH \diagdown \underset{\displaystyle R_2}{CH} \diagup CO \diagdown NH \diagup \underset{\displaystyle R_3}{CH} \diagdown COOH
$$

Polypeptides may contain a number of different amino-acids, but each may be represented more than once. The properties of the particular polypeptides—and proteins as well—depend on the identity and the sequence of acids along the chain.

The analogy with the carbohydrates, in which multiple condensation takes place to form long-chain molecules, is not entirely valid, as in the polypeptide chain the units of the chains are usually different, but nevertheless arranged in a specific series. How they come to take up this pattern and themselves become bonded together into even longer chains is a more difficult problem to solve.

X-ray analysis of structural proteins has shown that the amino-acid residues are arranged on alternate sides of the chain. These residues may be either acidic or basic (e.g. aspartic and glutamic acids are acidic, lysine and arginine basic), this leads to the possibility of linkages between two nearby chains. Links between amino groups and carboxyl groups are also found and are of a simple electrovalent type involving the removal of a positively charged hydrogen ion (proton) from the carboxyl group to the amino group:

Other commonly found linkages occur through sulphur atoms and through hydrogen bonding between hydrogen atoms and oxygen atoms:

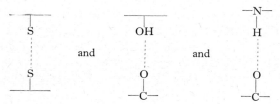

6.4 The organization of proteins and enzymes

There are three main groups of proteins, the *structural proteins*, the *reserve proteins* and the *enzymes*. The first group includes those that make up parts of the various cell organelles, the 'backbone' of the chromosomes on which the nucleic acids are arranged, the structural material of the mitochondria and some of the other cell organelles.

The reserve proteins are not used much as respiratory sources; they are often easily broken down into peptides and amino-acids, which are then translocated and metabolized into new structural or enzymatic proteins. For details of the analysis of proteins and amino-acids in germinating seeds and other tissues, see Appendix, p. 195.

The enzymes

Considerable attention has been devoted to the enzymes, the organic catalysts that assist almost all the reactions that go on in the cell. These are broadly classified into two groups, those that are *site-specific* and are an integral part of the mitochondria, chloroplasts, ribosomes and other cell organelles and those that exist *free* in the cytoplasm as minute colloidal particles.

Characteristics of enzymes

Many enzymes have now been at least partially *characterized*, that is, they have been extracted in a more or less pure state and information about their mode of action obtained. (An investigation of the enzyme polyphenol oxidase is discussed in the Appendix, p. 183.) These attempts to characterize different enzymes emphasize certain of their properties. Enzymes resemble inorganic catalysts in that they for the most part influence only the rate, and not the final equilibrium of the reaction.

Although enzymes are large, complex molecules, there is some evidence that they may possess only one site at which the reaction can take place. This *active centre* is thought to obtain some sort of 'fit' with the substrate so as to catalyse the reaction. The rate at which this catalysis may take place is exceedingly variable, some enzymes, e.g. catalase (which breaks down hydrogen peroxide into oxygen and water), work exceedingly fast, and each molecule of enzyme may be able to act on more than a million molecules of substrate in a minute. Other enzymes may have lower *turnover numbers*, being able to catalyse only a hundred or so molecules in a minute.

Some of the conditions which influence the activity of a particular enzyme are well known. Temperature affects the rate of enzyme-catalysed reactions; the Q_{10} for enzymatic reactions being about two, which is typical of most chemical reactions. Unlike inorganic catalysts, an enzyme has a *temperature optimum*, above which the rate of the reaction falls off until ultimately thermal inactivation takes place at about 60° C. The temperature curve for polyphenol oxidase is shown in fig. 6.10. The pH of the medium also affects the performance of the enzyme, most working best over a fairly narrow range. These features are particularly clear in experiments involving the characterization of enzymes, but it is less clear how such factors may affect the performance of enzymes operating in the intact cell.

Most enzymatic reactions are reversible and it is often difficult to understand how the same enzyme may affect a reaction in two directions. A good example of this is in the action of the enzyme triose-phosphate dehydrogenase. In photosynthesis this enzyme co-operates with TPNH to reduce PGA to triose (see p. 57), while in respiration triose may be converted into PGA in the opposite manner. Substrate availability and other factors in the area of the particular enzyme may determine the direction and rate of the catalysed reaction.

Enzymes, unlike many inorganic catalysts, show considerable *specificity*; some show *absolute specificity*, for instance catalase, which is only able to catalyse the breakdown of hydrogen peroxide into oxygen and water. Others are less specific and are capable of catalysing a series of reactions with different substances, because these substances all contain a particular group or bond.

Some enzymes are *stereo-specific*; for instance β-glycosidase hydrolyses β- but not α-glycosides to form alcohol and a sugar. On the other hand,

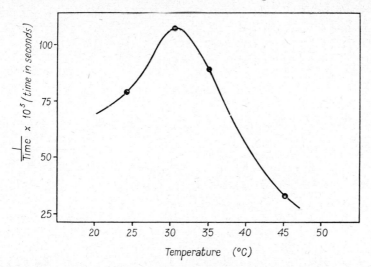

FIG. 6.10. Temperature curve for the activity of polyphenol oxidase. (Class result.)

this enzyme will attack a wide range of glycosides containing different alcohol groups. In short, like most enzymes, these are concerned with a particular bond or part of the molecule rather than with all the parts of the whole molecule.

Structure of enzymes

Many enzymes consist of a main protein part and non-protein or *prosthetic group* which can often be separated from the protein by dialysis. Coenzymes are prosthetic groups that are readily dissociated. Coenzyme II (TPN) is associated with many different enzymes, including many of those of respiration and photosynthesis (see p. 57 and p. 76). Enzymes may also include metallic *activator* groups which are also sometimes called coenzymes. Iron and copper in the respiratory cytochromes and ascorbic acid have already been discussed (p. 77). Specific inhibitors, e.g. cyanide, often act through forming stable complexes with these metallic groups. In this respect enzymes bear some relation to inorganic catalysts, which may be poisoned or rendered useless by the presence of impurities. *Competitive inhibitors*, e.g. fluoracetic acid (see p. 74), block reactions by resembling the normal substrate so closely that the enzyme forms an association with the inhibitor instead of the correct substrate and is unable to act. In this way enzymatic inhibitors are particularly useful for the investigation of reaction pathways.

6.5 Protein synthesis

The most likely mechanism of protein synthesis is that the RNA provides a blueprint or template on which the synthesis takes place. That this is likely is suggested by the treatment of cells with the enzyme ribonuclease. This enzyme, which breaks down ribonucleic acid, also usually inhibits the formation of new protein. Use of radioactive C14 labelled amino-acids indicates that peptides are themselves not particularly important in protein synthesis, as they seldom accumulate in more than trace amounts. On the other hand, it is possible that they are immediately converted into protein as they have a high turnover. However, the most likely conclusion must be that the amino-acids are synthesized together on one surface to form the protein direct. This occurs by means of peptide bonds, but seldom by the accumulation of free polypeptides.

Evidence regarding the site of this synthesis has come from the use of C14 together with fractional centrifuging techniques. Amino-acids containing C14 tracer are injected into a living tissue, which is then killed, ground up in isotonic ice-cold buffer and centrifuged slowly, at medium

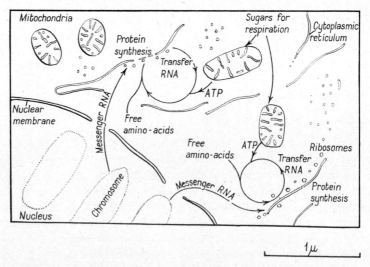

FIG. 6.11. Co-ordination of cell activities in protein synthesis.

speed and then at very high speeds of about 100,000 × g. It is found that only the RNA-rich microsomal fraction, thrown down at the last high speeds, contains the tracer, and the tracer is mostly incorporated into proteins. If the sampling is carried out soon after application of the radioactive amino-acids, then the ribosomes carry the tracer, but if the sampling is delayed for some time, then they are no longer radioactive. In other words, a fresh series of unlabelled amino-acids has been metabolized, the first having been released into the cytoplasm as proteins.

In the neighbourhood of the cytoplasmic reticulum and ribosomes (see fig. 6.11) there are already present free amino-acids, transfer RNA, ATP and certain enzymes. It is thought that an enzyme forms a surface for bringing these together, ATP providing the energy so as to form a complex of the enzyme, transfer RNA and the *appropriate* amino-acid (see fig. 6.12). The other form of RNA, messenger RNA, a replica of the DNA, consisting of larger numbers of nucleotides, also diffuses out of the nucleus, and takes up a position on the ribosome, where it forms a template for the protein synthesis. The smaller transfer RNA complexes then arrange themselves alongside the larger messenger RNA template, obtaining the right 'fit' in the process. In this way the correct amino-acids required for a particular protein or enzyme are brought together *in the correct sequence* as determined by the messenger RNA template, which is itself a replicate of the original nuclear DNA of the gene. Finally, the bond through which the amino-acid and transfer RNA were joined moves so as to effect peptide bond formation between each amino-acid. As this is accomplished the chain of amino-acids, now a protein, 'unzips' from the transfer RNA and the latter is released for further synthesis or is destroyed (see fig. 6.12).

This mechanism for protein synthesis—involving a transference of information from the nucleus to the ribosome site in the form of messenger RNA and requiring the co-operation of the mitochondria—emphasizes that the cell, to work efficiently, or indeed at all, must respond as an organized and integrated whole. The recent advances in biochemistry and electron microscopy have made it possible, for the first time, for us to visualize how at least some of these vital processes take place.

The genetic code

The year 1961 can be regarded as a milestone in the study of cell organization, as the work of Crick at Cambridge and Nirenberg in the United States has shown us something of the mechanism by which *different proteins* are produced by a given nucleotide complement on the chromosome. In other words, they have indicated some of the first steps in the sequence of *how genes act*.

Nirenberg's work has been based on the technique of extracting the ribosomes, feeding them with messenger RNA of a known base sequence

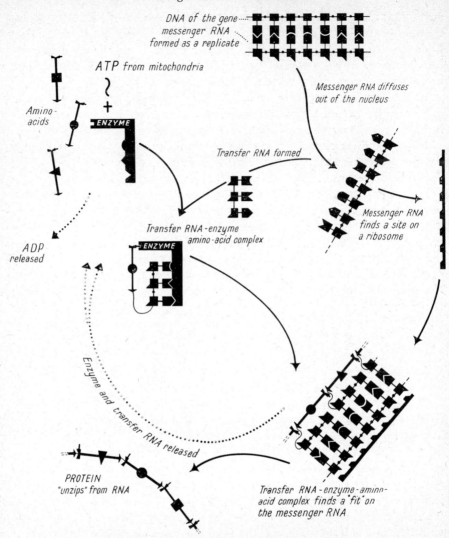

FIG. 6.12. The mechanism of protein synthesis.

Transfer RNA. Only three nucleotides are shown, the macromolecule is in fact much larger, though still smaller than the messenger RNA.

Transfer RNA-amino-acid complex. At the moment it is not clear what part of this complex does find a 'fit' on the messenger RNA.

and then analysing the amino-acid order of the protein produced. Analysis of RNA has shown that it can contain four bases, adenine, guanine, cytosine and uracil. If messenger RNA consisting of only *uracil* nucleotides is fed to the extracted ribosomes in the presence of the twenty or so amino-acids that are commonly found in the cytoplasm, then a protein is formed consisting of only one amino-acid type, *phenylalanine*. Similarly, a strand of messenger RNA composed of only *cytosine* groups produced a protein with only *proline* amino-acid units.

The next problem is *how many* nucleotide bases of the messenger RNA are required to order one amino-acid? With only four bases to select in the code and twenty amino-acids to form, two nucleotides would be too few, as only sixteen combinations can be produced by these bases. Three nucleotides might seem a likely number. Another problem relates to the reading of the code for the whole nucleotide sequence. Is there any indication where a set of the three nucleotides begins, or does the code simply start at one end of the nucleotide series and simply 'read along' counting off three nucleotides at a time?

The answers to these problems have come from Crick's work on a virus which attacks bacteria, called the T4 bacteriophage. This was treated with proflavine, a chemical mutagen that causes deletion or addition of a nucleotide base, so that it would not attack one of two strains of bacteria. By careful use of the mutagen they were able to show that the code reads from one end of a DNA chain. First a mutation was caused near the start of the nucleotide sequence; this mutant will only attack one strain of bacteria. A second mutation was caused in the bacteriophage close to the site of the first mutation which would 'displace the type' of the code so that the effect of the first mutation was removed (see below). Mutations farther along the nucleotide sequence would still not be fully viable, as the order of nucleotides has been upset by the first mutation, near the start of the sequence. The new mutation must be near the first if the correct order of sufficient nucleotides is to be restored.

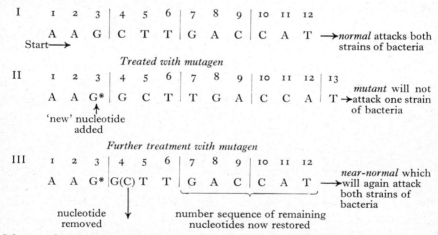

Scheme to show that the reading of the genetic code of nucleotides depends on reading the whole sequence from one end (Hypothetical DNA nucleotide sequence)

A=adenine, G=guanine, C=cytosine, T=thymine

I

Similarly, the virus could be made to change back to the normal type by introducing *two more mutations*, both of which add another nucleotide to the sequence.

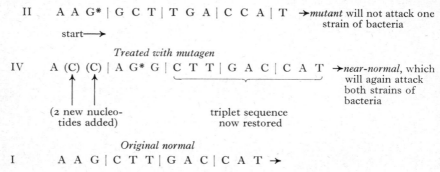

II   A A G* | G C T | T G A | C C A | T   →*mutant* will not attack one
    start——→   strain of bacteria

Treated with mutagen
IV   A (C) (C) | A G* G | C T T | G A C | C A T   →*near-normal*, which
                                                      will again attack
                                                      both strains of
                                                      bacteria

    (2 new nucleo-   triplet sequence
    tides added)   now restored

Original normal
I   A A G | C T T | G A C | C A T →

Scheme to show that the reading of the genetic code is carried out in groups of three nucleotides at a time
The sequence of nucleotides in each triplet is the same in the final mutant (IV) as in the normal (I)

The code of nucleotides on the messenger or template RNA that determines the selection of a particular amino-acid for incorporation into a particular protein is thus at least partially understood, and we are much nearer an understanding of how a particular gene produces a particular protein. However, many problems remain; we have little idea how the system is integrated and how different instructions may be given as cell-division and differentiation proceed. Nevertheless, the decoding of some steps in the sequence of protein synthesis must remain an important step in the history of biology.

6.6 Carbohydrate chemistry

In Chapter 3 we discussed the formation of the main product of photosynthesis, fructose-diphosphate. This substance is converted into a wide range of structural and energy-reserve carbohydrates and carbohydrate derivatives which are of great importance in the organization of the cell.

Structure of sugar molecules

There are two outstanding features of carbohydrate conversions that must be considered from the outset, first, the isomeric properties of the hexose unit, and secondly, the conversions which take place involving the phosphate ester of the particular sugar.

Fructose, for example, can exist in two isomeric forms, one being the six-sided pyranose ring, which is more usual, the other being the more reactive, less stable, five-cornered furanose form:

fructopyranose   fructofuranose

The numbers indicate the standard numbering of each carbon atom. In addition to these two isomers there are also *stereoisomers*. In these there is only a spatial difference; for example, glucopyranose can exist in two forms, α- and β-glucopyranose. These can be distinguished by their differing abilities to rotate the plane of polarized light (see notes on the use of the polarimeter in Appendix, p. 197). Both are dextro-rotatory, but the α-form more strongly so that the β-form:

α-glucopyranose   β-glucopyranose

These various isomeric forms are of considerable importance, as in the combination of fructofuranose and glucopyranose in sucrose synthesis; in the formation of polysaccharides, by condensation of α-glucopyranose units giving starch. Similarly the condensation of β-glucopyranose units gives cellulose.

Attention has already been drawn to the formation of phosphate esters of sugars in both photosynthesis and respiration; few carbohydrate conversions take place unless the hexoses are in the form of the phosphate esters. This is probably because many reactions require the co-operation of enzymes capable only of working on the phosphate esters. Looked at another way, one could say that the formation of the phosphate ester from the ordinary hexose sugar requires high-energy phosphate (ATP), and this, through the addition of the phosphate radical, is necessary for the eventual condensation. The final product of photosynthesis may be regarded as fructofuranose-diphosphate. A vast range of more complex substances are made from this substance as the essential starting-point; the reserve carbohydrates, the structural carbohydrates, the vacuolar pigments and the glycosides. As most of these are vitally important in the cell, it is necessary to know how and where they are formed.

6.7　The reserve carbohydrates

The two most important of these carbohydrates, which are easily utilized as food and energy sources, are the disaccharide sucrose ($C_{12}H_{22}O_{11}$) and the polysaccharide starch. In many plants these are formed quickly and directly from the fructose produced in photosynthesis.

Sucrose

Sucrose is formed by a combination of fructofuranose-6-phosphate with glucopyranose-6-phosphate:

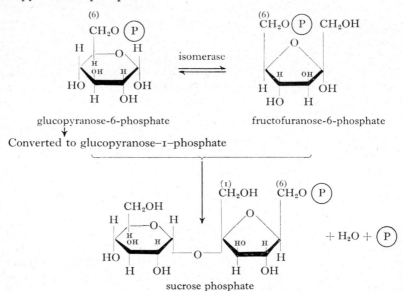

glucopyranose-6-phosphate　　　　　　　　fructofuranose-6-phosphate

Converted to glucopyranose–1–phosphate

sucrose phosphate

This synthesis requires a condensing enzyme and uridine-triphosphate. The overall reaction requires energy derived from the conversion of ATP to ADP.

The sucrose can be hydrolysed to form glucose and fructose by the enzyme invertase or quite simply in the laboratory by the action of dilute acid. As these products have different optical properties (glucose being weakly dextro-rotatory, fructose laevo-rotatory), the activity of the enzyme invertase can be examined in the polarimeter (see Appendix, p. 197). The sucrose is strongly dextro-rotatory, and the final product or invert sugar mixture is weakly laevo-rotatory. Although some plants, particularly sugar beet and sugar-cane, store large quantities of sucrose, it is not usually the primary reserve carbohydrate. Owing to its solubility and consequent ease of transport, it is found in the cytoplasm of many cells and may be transported considerable distances (for instance, to the nectaries of flowers) through the phloem elements.

Starch

In all essentials starch is probably a long-chain condensation product which can be formed from glucose-1-phosphate molecules by the action of starch phosphorylase (though other enzymes are also capable of effecting the synthesis).

Synthesis of amylose by the formation of 1–4 α links between glucose molecules

Synthesis of amylopectin by the formation of 1–6 α links between glucose molecules

This simple starch involving 1–4 α links between the glucose units is called amylose. This reaction can be carried out in the laboratory using an enzyme extract obtained from potato (see Appendix, p. 198). Starch also consists of a second substance, amylopectin, in which there are 1–6 α links, as well as the 1–4 α links, the former are produced due to the activity of a so-called *branching enzyme*.

In amylopectin each branch may consist of between twenty and thirty glucose units, but the overall macromolecule may have been formed from hundreds of hexose molecules.

Starch must generally rate as the most important storage carbohydrate in plant cells, and small grains of it are usually visible in the chloroplast itself soon after photosynthesis has begun in an illuminated leaf. Accumulated starch in storage organs, such as rhizomes and tubers, is another problem, as it must necessitate the conversion of the starch into soluble material that can be easily translocated both to and from the storage organ.

Translocation of carbohydrates

The path of translocation of such soluble carbohydrates is through the phloem. This has been shown by experiments detecting C^{14} labelled photosynthetic products which have been formed by allowing a leaf to photosynthcsize for several hours in an atmosphere containing $C^{14}O_2$. The sugars (mostly sucrose) produced are eventually translocated down the petiole to storage structures and the root, and upwards to the stem apex and growing leaves. If a heat jacket, which will coagulate the proteins of the living phloem cells, is applied around the petiole, then translocation is prevented. The xylem is relatively unaffected by such treatments, which indicate that translocation of sugars takes place through the living protoplasm of the phloem. Once the sugars reach the storage organs they must be converted into starch by the multiple condensation reactions described above. Starch is converted into soluble sugars by the action of a group of hydrolysing enzymes called the amylases.

6.8   The structural carbohydrates

The carbohydrates also play a vital role in plants in providing their cells with strength. The simplest of these structural substances is cellulose, but in some tissues this may become replaced by the more complex lignin.

The cellulose macromolecule is superficially similar to that of amylose, but β-glucopyranose units are joined by 1·4 β links. This type of linkage results in extremely long-chain macromolecules which may contain as many as 2,500 glucose residues. Additional strength is given to the molecule by hydrogen bonding between the hydroxyl groups of the different chains; in this way the cellulose takes up a crystalline form and chains of great tensile strength are built up. The arrangement of these chains in the cell is of considerable interest. The middle lamella, that is the layer between the primary walls of two adjoining layers, is composed of a mixture of

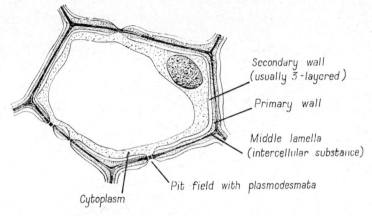

calcium and magnesium pectates (see below) and forms a non-crystalline, colloidal layer. The primary wall is the next to be formed by the growing

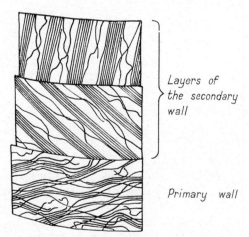

Fig. 6.13. The cell wall constituents of the parenchymatous cell.

Fig. 6.14. Arrangement of microfibrils of cellulose in the outer layers of the cell wall.

cell, and consists mostly of cellulose, together with various pectic compounds. As the cell grows various cellulose layers are laid down, and this may result in the formation of obvious laminations. Finally, when the cell has ceased to enlarge, the formation of the secondary cell wall may take place, and this, like the primary wall, also consists mainly of cellulose (see figs. 6.13 and 6.14).

Cellulose serves a vital role in the cell in enclosing the whole protoplasm and acting as a strong, yet fully permeable, elastic boundary wall.

Pectic substances

An important group of carbohydrate derivatives that are often found impregnating the cell wall and even in the cytoplasm of the cell are the pectins or pectic substances. These are also polymers, but are derivatives of the sugar, galactose, through the formation of galacturonic acid. Residues of galacturonic acid are joined together by series of condensations like those found in the formation of starch and cellulose.

Galacturonic acid units

pectic acid

The pectic acid chain will then react with calcium and magnesium ions to form insoluble pectates. These divalent ions act as bridges between separate pectic acid chains and so add to the strength of the whole.

Lignin

Under certain circumstances, for instance, in fibres and sclerenchymatous cells, parts of the cell wall may become progressively impregnated by the more complex carbohydrate lignin. It may be present in all three cell layers. Lignification usually starts from the outside of the cell, and in heavily lignified areas it is usual to find the middle lamella and primary wall most strongly thickened.

Structurally lignin is in some ways similar to cellulose, being composed of a number of molecules or monomers joined together in long chains. The formation and identity of the lignin monomer is still in doubt, but its main part is constructed not of a carbohydrate residue, but of an aromatic unit. These are possibly synthesized from glucose through a series of cyclic compounds including shikimic acid. Evidence that this is so comes from work in which this acid, radioactively labelled, was fed to the leaves of sugar-cane plants; analysis of the lignin showed that it had accumulated the tracer that had been in the shikimic acid.

Simple lignin monomer

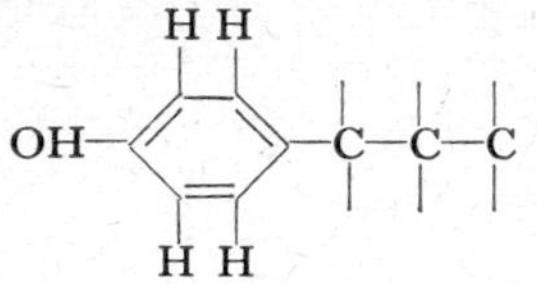

$$OH-\langle\rangle-C-C-C$$

So while the complete structure of the polymer is still largely unknown, it seems likely that lignin consists of a number of aromatic monomers formed originally from carbohydrates.

6.9 The glycosides; the anthocyanins

This is a group of complex carbohydrate derivatives which is found commonly in plants but whose role is often rather obscure. They may be of use as food reserve substances, or in some cases may be regarded as by-products of metabolism. The group includes the water-soluble vacuolar pigments, the anthocyanins and anthoxanthins, which may be of considerable importance to the plant in the form of flower colours and autumnal pigmentation. Glycosides are hydrolysed by dilute mineral acids and by the various enzymes; the hydrolysis products being most usually glucose, together with various other substances. For instance, the cyanogenic glycosides, which are common in almonds, cherry-laurel leaves and white clover, yield glucose and hydrocyanic acid.

The anthocyanins

Because of the importance of the anthocyanins in the colouring of flowers and leaves, considerable interest has been devoted to their structure, formation and properties. They are formed from a non-sugar or anthocyanidin portion, which accounts for most of their colour, together with various sugar units. The sugars make the pigments more soluble in water.

The anthocyanidin nucleus

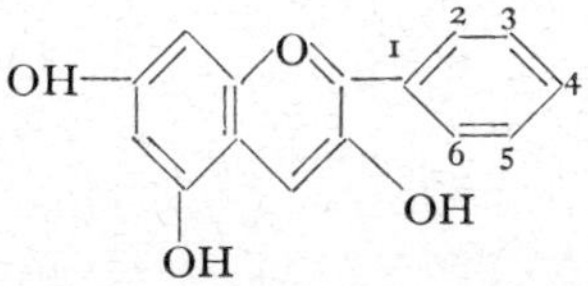

The three simplest anthocyanidins; pelargonidin; cyanidin and delphinidin, have hydroxyl groups substituted into the lateral benzene ring. Pelargonidin, the red pigment named after *Pelargonium* (geranium), has the hydroxyl substituted in the 4-position. Cyanidin, the blue-violet pigment, is one of the commonest anthocyanins and is found in *Centaurea cyanus*

(cornflower) and has the 3- and 4-hydroxyl groups substituted. Delphinidin, the deep-blue pigment that occurs in the delphinium and other flowers, has substitution in the 3-, 4- and 5-hydroxyl groups.

Pelargonidin   Cyanidin

Delphinidin

Just as an increase in hydroxylation gives added blueness to the pigment, substitution of the hydrogen of the hydroxyl group by a methyl group tends to have the reverse effect. Substitution of hydroxyl groups by methyl groups tends therefore to make the colour slightly more red:

Cyanidin   Peonidin
(blue-violet)   (crimson-purple)

The final way in which the colour can be changed is by substitution of hydroxyl groups of the main part of the anthocyanidin molecule with sugars. Addition of two such sugar molecules tends to increase the intensity of blueness. For instance, the scarlet pigment pelargonidin becomes a scarlet-magenta.

In most flowers there are mixtures of several pigments; for instance, it is usual to find *anthoxanthins* (see below) and different anthocyanins together. The actual colour of the petals may depend on the relative proportions of these pigments, as well as various physical factors, such as the pH of the cell sap; anthocyanins are red in acid solution and blue in alkali. Full details for the separation and identification of these pigments are given in the Appendix, p. 199.

Particular interest has been attached to the genetics of flower colours. In most species the presence or absence of a particular hydroxyl group, methyl group or sugar can be related to the effect of a particular gene. In the gloxinia-like greenhouse plant *Streptocarpus* a wide range of flower colours is controlled by four separate gene loci, so as to give a colour range from ivory to deep blue. If all four genes are present only in their recessive states the colour is ivory, no anthocyanins being formed. When the alleles are replaced by their dominant forms various methyl groups are added or substituted into the lateral benzene ring, and at the same time various sugars are substituted into the main part of the molecule:

Colour	Gene Complement	Anthocyanidin	Structure
Ivory	aarroodd	None present	
Salmon	A-rroodd	Form of pelargonidin	
Pink	A-rrooD-	Form of pelargonidin	
Magenta	A-R-ooD-	Peonidin	
Blue	A-R-O-D-	Malvidin	

A number of other gene combinations is also possible. This is a particularly clear example of the way in which a number of genes control the variation in a plant characteristic.

The anthoxanthins

These are closely related chemically to the anthocyanins and are common water-soluble vacuolar pigments. Unlike the anthocyanins, with which they are often found, the anthoxanthins show little colour range, being almost colourless in neutral or acid solution and yellow or orange in alkaline. They are more common in leaves and photosynthesizing tissues, though their presence is often noticed only in the autumn when the ether-soluble chlorophyll pigments are bleached.

Autumnal coloration

Many plants, such as the copper beech and species of maple, have varieties which possess a large amount of anthocyanin in their leaves throughout the year. In most plants, however, there is very little or none until the autumn, when the brilliant tints that are so often found are due to extensive changes in the pigment distribution in the leaf. Analysis of the ether-soluble and water-soluble pigments shows that of the former group the chlorophylls are bleached at the beginning of the visible colour change.   Later

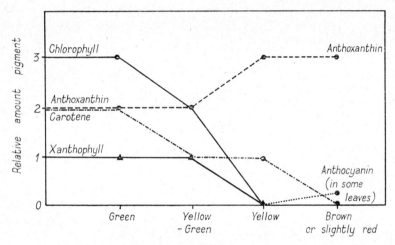

FIG. 6.15. Changes in the leaf pigments during autumnal coloration in the plane tree (*Platanus* × *hybrida*).

the carotenoid pigments, xanthophyll and carotene disappear. During this time there tends to be an accumulation of the anthoxanthin which results in the leaf taking on a yellow colour, partly due to carotenoids that are still remaining and also to the accumulating anthoxanthin. During these last stages anthocyanins may also appear. There is, of course, considerable variation from plant to plant; the pigment changes for *Platanus* × *hybrida* (the plane tree) are given in the graph, fig. 6.15. During this colour change, marked changes in the metabolism of the leaf take place. The bleaching of the chlorophyll results in a cessation of photosynthesis, very little starch being formed even in leaves that are brightly illuminated. At the same time the RQ (see p. 65) begins to fall, and it is therefore thought that the formation of anthocyanins has a high demand on oxygen; the RQ values, determined manometrically, may be as low as 0·5.

6.10 Lipid (fat) metabolism

Although the carbohydrates tend to be regarded as the most general and important of the food-reserve substances in plants, this is sometimes an erroneous view, engendered perhaps by our use of cereal crops for food. For the most part only the grasses and leguminous crops make use of starch as their food-reserve substance in seeds, the vast majority of seeds containing lipids or fats as their food-reserve material. In addition, these may accumulate in young tissues and in the leaves, for instance large fat globules are visible in the stomatal guard cells of the privet, and many fungi and algae use lipids as their main food reserve. Phospholipids are an important group of fats that combine both water-loving (hydrophilic) and water-repellant properties. They are often found in the cell-membranes, the plasma membrane and the tonoplast, where their bipolar structure gives the membrane its characteristic properties.

Structurally, fats and oils are derivatives of glycerol and fatty acids. Glycerol is a three-carbon alcohol which is derived from three carbon (triose) sugars:

$$
\begin{array}{ccc}
\text{CH}_2\text{OH} & \text{ADP} \qquad \text{ATP} & \text{CH}_2\text{OH} \\
| & & | \\
\text{CO} & \longrightarrow & \text{CHOH} \\
| & & | \\
\text{CH}_2\text{O}\ \textcircled{P} & \text{DPNH}_2 \qquad \text{DPN} & \text{CH}_2\text{OH} \\
\text{triose} & & \text{glycerol} \\
\text{phosphate} & &
\end{array}
$$

A wide range of fatty acids is formed in plant tissues, but the commonest include palmitic acid, stearic acid and oleic acid, e.g.

$$\text{CH}_3(\text{CH}_2)_{14}\text{COOH} \quad . \qquad . \qquad . \;\; \text{Palmitic acid}$$

The formation of a fat is essentially one of esterification through the union of the acid with the alcohol:

$$
\begin{array}{ll}
\text{CH}_2\text{OH} & \text{CH}_2\text{O}(\text{C}_{15}\text{H}_{31}\text{CO}) \\
| & | \\
\text{CHOH} + 3 . \text{C}_{15}\text{H}_{31}\text{COOH} \longrightarrow & \text{CHO}(\text{C}_{15}\text{H}_{31}\text{CO}) + 3\text{H}_2\text{O} \\
| & | \\
\text{CH}_2\text{OH} & \text{CH}_2\text{O}(\text{C}_{15}\text{H}_{31}\text{CO}) \\
\text{glycerol} + \text{palmitic acid} \longrightarrow & \text{palmitin} + \text{water}
\end{array}
$$

The second group of lipids, the waxes, differ from fats and oils in that the glycerol is replaced by monohydric or occasionally dihydric alcohols. These substances are important in that they line the epidermis of a wide range of plants, lowering cuticular transpiration. Electron-microscope photographs of the surfaces of leaves show some of the beautiful arrangements that these waxy layers may form (see fig. 2.11 on p. 22). Cutin and suberin are wax-like substances also found in epidermal layers and are the condensation products of various fatty acids. Such substances also occur in the Casparian strip of the endodermis, where they are important in preventing the movement of water and solutes through the cell walls. Details of simple tests for lipids are given in the Appendix, p. 201.

The pathway for the formation of the fatty acids is complex, but it is thought that they are formed from acid intermediates such as acetyl-coenzyme A, the acetic acid derivative formed at the start of the Citric Acid Cycle (see p. 72).

6.11   Integration of cell processes

In this chapter we have discussed the formation and properties of some of the classes of organic substance that are found in living organisms, the nucleic acids, proteins, carbohydrates and lipids. Among these bio-chemical details it must still be realised that the cell works as an organized whole, the nucleic acids of the chromosome form the blueprint for order-ing the sequence of the various metabolic processes that are going on, by controlling the production of the enzymes and proteins. The process of photosynthesis in the chloroplasts provides the simple sugars that are the chief means for assimilating carbon into the plant and at the same time provide the plant with its energy. Respiration in the mitochondria releases the energy in the form of ATP, so that it can be used for most of the meta-bolic processes of the cell. At the same time respiration provides acids which are the starting-point in amino-acid and protein synthesis. Some of these proteins act as enzymes which may enable still further metabolic processes to take place. Yet these, too, are produced to the plan of the DNA of the chromosomes; specific nucleotides of a gene indicating specific proteins or enzymes in the cytoplasm. In some cases the effects of single genes may be apparent in the macro-structure of the plant, for instance, in flower colours, but more often their effects pass unnoticed as part of the vital processes going on in the cell.

7 Physiological Organization within the Plant

7.1 Introduction

In the preceding chapters we have tried to dissect out the various vital processes going on in the plant and have attempted to show how these are co-ordinated within the single cell; in this final chapter we have to show how the plant grows and responds as a single organized entity. First, there is the problem of development, involving division and differentiation from a single fertilized egg with a definite gene content, into a complex and specialized adult plant containing many types of cells. In the second place it must be realized that what a plant looks like, and how it behaves internally, are products of the interaction between two groups of factors; the plant's genes, which determine its potential shape, size and metabolism; and also the environment with all its different factors, which may affect and alter the plant considerably, yet within the limits set by the genotype of the plant.

7.2 The problem of growth and differentiation

As growth proceeds in any young structure, such as the root apex, definite phases of differentiation are clearly visible. In the first phase, involving rapid cell-division, there is considerable manufacture of new protein material, but the increase in size before the next division is not great. In the second phase the beginnings of differentiation are visible, the cells rarely divide and they begin to develop and differentiate into a type of 'adult' cell. This phase may involve considerable elongation and vacuolation, as well as considerable protein synthesis. If the cell is to become one of the vascular elements, for instance a phloem sieve tube, the end walls of the cell become sieve-plates and the cell's own nucleus is broken down. Only a few cells distant the xylem elements differentiate in an entirely different way, eventually having lignified cell walls but no protoplasm. Yet these two sorts of cells were formed from meristematic and elongating cells that were very similar. A similar process, which is still more difficult to explain, occurs in the cells produced by cambium activity. Apparently identical cells produce xylem elements by division to one side and phloem by division to the other. How, then, does this origin of form or *morpho-*

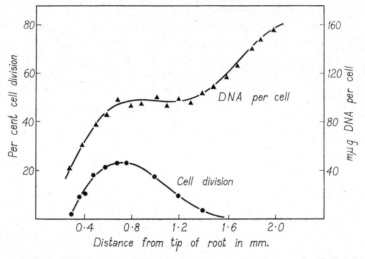

Fig. 7.1. Relationship between DNA content per cell and rate of cell division in an onion root tip. (After Jensen, W. A. (1963). *Plant Biology Today.* London, Macmillan.)

genesis of cells that would appear to be genetically identical take place? Obviously there are two groups of factors involved. First there are the genetic factors, or those concerning the nucleus and the nucleic acids. Second, there is the 'environment' in which the cells are found. The more we can find out about the action and inter-play of these factors, the more we may find out about morphogenesis.

Recently Linderstrøm-Lang has evolved techniques for the chemical analysis of the cell constituents of very small segments of roots. In one experiment of this sort carried out by Jensen et al., the DNA content per cell was analysed continuously back from the root apex. It was found that the DNA content continued to rise in the elongating area, after cell division had more or less ceased (see fig. 7.1). This suggested that some cells might have become *polyploid*; that is doubled or increased their chromosome number without cell division. We may therefore have to discard our concept of genetically identical cells occurring throughout the plant. These histochemical techniques are now being extended to investigate small changes in RNA, protein and enzyme content of the cells.

When a cell is part of a tissue it must be influenced by the surrounding cells in a large number of ways. One of the most important of these is through the action of a wide range of substances referred to as *hormones*.

An example of a secretion produced by one cell which will subsequently influence the development of another is found in the slime-mould or social amoeba, *Dictyostelium discoideum*. This is a remarkable organism that

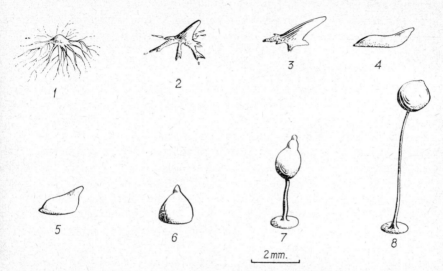

FIG. 7.2. Differentiation in the social amoeba (*Dictyostelium discoideum*) from the coming together of free-living amoebae to the formation of the spore mass. (After Bonner: Differentiation in Social Amoebae. *Scientific American*. Dec., 1959, p. 156.)

exists as free-living amoebae (see fig. 7.2) that aggregate into a motile 'slug' that then differentiates to form a fruiting body. Although all the amoebae that come together to form an individual slug seem to be genetic-ally identical, the larger tend to become the stalk of the fruiting body and the smaller the spores. The problem is, how are these amoebae organized together into this co-ordinated mass? The organism produces a secretion called *acrasin* which stimulates the amoebae to congregate. They respond not only by movement towards one another but also by producing more acrasin themselves. This will tend to influence more outlying amoebae.

Investigation of the effect of the various factors of the external environ-ment on the growth and development of plants has provided a great deal of information as to how plant hormones control the pattern of growth.

K

7.3 The influence of the environment on growth and development

From the moment a seed alights on the ground, it is at the mercy of the environment. It will not germinate unless the suitable oxygen, water and temperature conditions exist, nor will it develop and flower unless it receives sufficient light, water, minerals and nutrients. Yet the environment can only affect the plant within the latter's genetically imposed limits. For instance, the prostrate form of the broom (*Sarothamnus scoparius* ssp. *maritimus*), which grows on exposed cliffs, will remain dwarf and flat-growing under all environmental conditions. However, the scarlet pimpernel (*Anagallis arvensis*) shows considerable *phenotypic variation* and under marsh conditions may become conspicuously succulent (see p. 31).

7.4 The effect of light

Of all the environmental factors that may affect growth and development, one of the best understood is light. It should not be forgotten that the growth rate may be determined by light, through determining the amount of photosynthesis; consequently adaptations that will enable a plant to obtain more light may have high survival value. For instance, it is frequently observed that plants on a window-sill bend towards light and also that forest trees tend to grow upwards straighter and faster under a more or less closed canopy. This bending of a plant towards light is termed *positive phototropism*. As it must clearly involve a unified response of a large number of cells, it is an interesting and important example of plant organization.

A series of simple experiments can be carried out to investigate the phototropic response. Young oat seedlings make useful experimental material, as their coleoptiles (sheaths protecting the leaves) are particularly light sensitive. They are also useful as few cell divisions occur and most of the later growth in the coleoptile is due to cell elongation. The first problem is to find what part of the coleoptile is light sensitive. If its apex is decapitated no phototropic response results. That this is not simply due to damage can be shown by decapitating and then replacing the apex, which will then respond in the normal way. That light does in some way affect the apex can be confirmed by covering it with a small tinfoil cap, and again no response results. These two tests suggest that some substance is produced by the apex, which diffuses down the coleoptile and could then do one (or both) of two things. It could cause inhibition of elongation on the light-treated side or, alternatively, promote elongation on the darker side; both effects would cause the observed bending. A third test can answer this point. This time the apex is decapitated and then replaced on top of two small agar blocks separated by a thin piece of mica or tinfoil (see fig. 7.3). The coleoptile is then illuminated for one or two hours from one side, and then the agar jelly blocks are removed and placed separately on two decapitated coleoptiles which are not illuminated. They are placed in similar positions to those that they occupied on the original coleoptile. The coleoptile with the agar block from the dark side is the only one to respond. This indicates that under these conditions some substance which

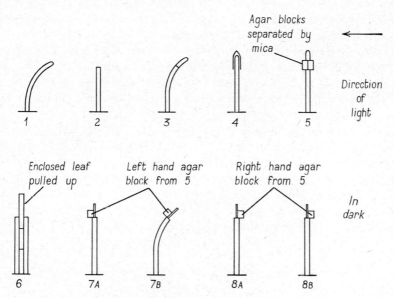

FIG. 7.3. The response of the oat coleoptile to light.

1. A coleoptile responds by bending towards light.
2. A decapitated coleoptile shows no response.
3. A decapitated coleoptile which has had its apex replaced bends towards the light.
4. A coleoptile with its apex covered by a tinfoil cap shows no response.
5. A coleoptile has its apex separated from the rest by two agar blocks separated by a piece of mica.
6. Shows how a decapitated coleoptile, with its enclosed leaf, is prepared for agar block treatment.
7A. The left-hand block is placed on a freshly prepared coleoptile.
7B. This shows a typical positive phototropism, indicating that auxin is present in the side away from light and causes elongation.
8A. The right-hand block is placed on a freshly prepared coleoptile.
8B. This shows no response, auxin formation being inhibited by light.

seems to be destroyed by light diffuses out of the apex, though in the intact plant there is some evidence that auxin may diffuse laterally, away from the illuminated side.

When plants are grown in the dark the stems are thin and etiolated due to the cells becoming particularly elongated. This seems to indicate that some substance is produced evenly around the apex that promotes elongation. Light seems to have the sole effect of destroying the substance so as to cause less elongation and a consequent bending.

7.5 The auxins

The next problem is to identify the substance produced. If several apices are decapitated and placed on a block of agar jelly, then the substance diffuses into the agar. Analysis of this plant hormone *or auxin†* has shown it to be largely β-indolylacetic acid (IAA).

The investigation of the effect of concentration of IAA on elongation of cells has produced some rather surprising results which have had important agricultural and horticultural consequences. It was found that the auxin caused cell elongation only at extremely low concentrations. In most stems and coleoptiles maximum elongation is obtained at one part per million, and inhibition usually occurs above ten parts per million (see figs. 7.4 and 7.5, also Appendix, p. 202). As different plants have different tolerances for auxin, the grasses being able to tolerate a higher concentration of most auxins than broad-leaved plants, this inhibiting property opened up the important new field of selective weed-killers. One such weed-killer is 2,4-D (2,4-dichlorophenoxyacetic acid) and it is interesting to compare the formula of the natural substance with that of the weed-killer:

IAA   2,4–D

Other problems are how is this natural auxin (IAA) formed and how does light destroy it? It is thought that the apices contain the enzyme system necessary for forming the IAA from the amino-acid tryptophane.

Tryptophane   IAA

Clearly the conversion of the active IAA into an inactive form is a light-requiring reaction, and so there must be some light-absorbing pigment in the apex capable of initiating the conversion. The wavelength of light that

† Hormones are generally regarded as substances that are produced naturally and have effects on tissues some distance from the site where they are produced; in this chapter the term *auxin* is used for *all* growth-regulating substances, natural or artificial, including IAA, a substance which may also have effect on the cell in which it is formed

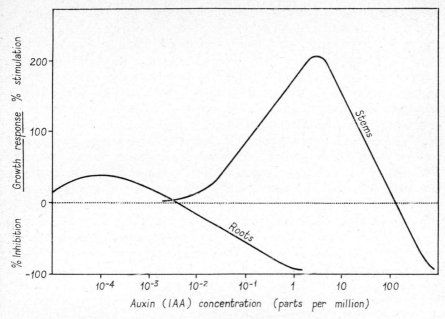

FIG. 7.4. The effect of auxin concentration on growth of root and stem.
(After Audus: *Plant Growth Substances.* London: Leonard Hill.)

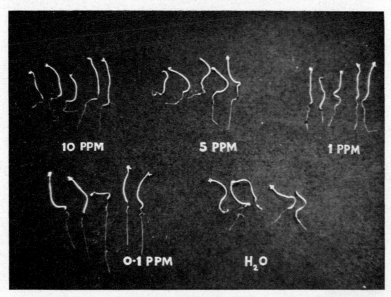

FIG. 7.5. The effect of indolylbutyric acid (IBA) on the growth of cress seedlings.
(Class result.)

is most effective in causing the phototropic response is about 450 mμ in the blue end of the spectrum. The only pigments which absorb light in this region of the spectrum that occur in the oat coleoptile are riboflavin and carotene, which both have a maximum light absorption very near this wavelength. It looks, then, as though the light energy absorbed by these pigments is somehow utilized in the destruction of the IAA, possibly via the activation of the enzyme IAA oxidase, which is known to break it down.

Recently other auxin-like substances, including the *gibberellins*, have been isolated from several plants. The effect of these substances was first realized under rather peculiar circumstances: in Japan rice is sometimes attacked by the parasitic fungus *Gibberella fujikuroi*; this causes a stimulation of growth in the rice, which becomes spindly and pale-coloured. Investigation of the parasite showed that it produced powerful growth-stimulating substances which have been named gibberellins. The effect of the gibberellins is particularly notable on dwarf strains; for instance, genetically dwarf strains of pea can be stimulated to grow to the size of genetically tall plants by application of a low concentration of gibberellic acid (see fig. 7.6). It seems likely that like IAA, the gibberellins occur widely in plant tissues and co-operate with IAA in controlling growth (see Appendix, p. 202). That they are of relatively low effect in the absence of IAA can be shown by estimation of the elongation of dwarf strain pea internodes in 0·1 part per million gibberellic acid with and without the same concentration of IAA. Another group of plant hormones have been discovered recently; these are the *kinins*. They seem to be particularly important in influencing the rate of mitosis and are found in young developing tissues and embryos. The kinins were first extracted from coconut milk and analysis has shown them to be largely composed of nucleotides such as adenine. It is probable that they co-operate with other plant hormones in determining rates of growth and development.

Most of the auxin substances are not limited in their effects to promoting or inhibiting the elongation of cells but also have pronounced influence on the day-to-day and year-to-year plant development and rhythm. They must therefore rate as one of the most important of cell co-ordinating substances in plants.

7.6   The control of flowering

As well as influencing the general shape of the plant through phototropic responses, light also has a vitally important effect on flowering, probably again by influencing hormonal changes in the growing apex.

It has been known since the 1920s that plants can be classified into three main groups according to the day-length periods that they require for flower induction. This phenomenon is referred to as *photoperiodism* (see fig. 7.7). Plants that require long days and short nights to induce flowering

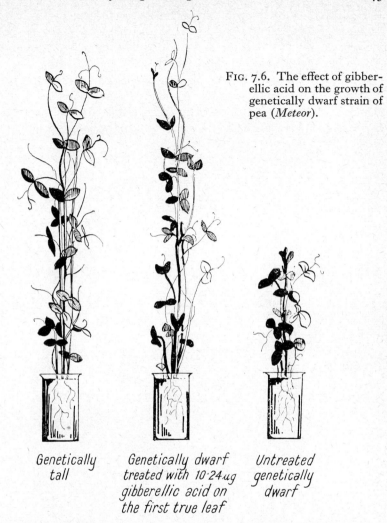

Fig. 7.6. The effect of gibberellic acid on the growth of
genetically dwarf strain of
pea (*Meteor*).

Genetically
tall

Genetically dwarf
treated with 10·24µg
gibberellic acid on
the first true leaf

Untreated
genetically
dwarf

are called long-day plants; the reverse are short-day plants, requiring a
maximum of about twelve hours daylight; the third group are neutral
or indifferent and may flower throughout the year. The table below lists a
few plants in each group:

Day length	Examples
Short	*Chrysanthemum*, cocklebur (*Xanthium*)
	Salvia, Maryland Mammoth tobacco
Long	*Petunia*, barley (*Hordeum*), spinach
Neutral	tomato, dandelion (*Taraxacum*)

This division of plants follows closely their geographic distribution. Long-day plants, which are normally summer flowering, are frequently found in Arctic and northern areas, where the summer is short and the day length very long indeed, while the short-day plants are more common nearer the Equator, and tend to be autumn or spring flowering.

The problem is, how does day (or night) length affect the plant so as to change the normal leaf primordia of the stem apex into flowering primordia? In short-day plants evidence that it is the dark period rather than the light

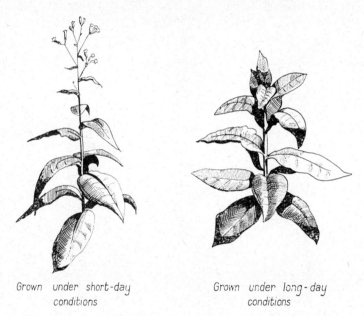

Grown under short-day   Grown under long-day
     conditions   conditions

Fig. 7.7. The effect of day length on flowering of tobacco (Maryland Mammoth). (From *Principles of Plant Physiology* by James Bonner & Arthur W. Galston. San Francisco: W. H. Freeman & Co., 1952. *After* Garner & Allard: *Year-book of Agriculture*, 1920.)

period which is important comes from experiments in which plants, treated with the appropriate day length, are given a short bright light flash in the middle of the night; this inhibits flowering. This phenomenon has been used commercially to retard the flowering of autumn-flowering *Chrysanthemum* so that they bloom at Christmas. The number of cycles of day plus night that are required to cause flowering is quite small; cocklebur (*Xanthium*) requires only one cycle, but most plants require about ten.

In long-day plants it can hardly be the dark period which is important, as they will flower in continuous daylight, so there must be different systems operating in the two groups.

Considerable work has been carried out recently on the nature of this photoperiodic induction. In the first place it was found that only red light (660 mμ) was effective in inhibiting the flowering of short-day plants when they received a light flash in the middle of the night. The same wavelength also tended to stimulate stem and root growth and anthocyanin formation in many plants.

The next step came when it was found that any inhibition could be reversed if the plants were treated with far-red light, at 735 mμ. This reversibility suggests that a single photoreceptive compound, which has been called *phytochrome*, is involved. This exists in two forms, designated P_{735} and P_{660}. When P_{660} is illuminated at 660 mμ it is transformed to the P_{735} form, and when P_{735} is illuminated at 735 mμ it reverts to the P_{660} form. During the dark P_{735} is slowly converted into the P_{660} form, and at the end of a normal day-period the predominant form is P_{735} because sunlight contains more orange-red light of wavelength 660 mμ.

This dark conversion to P_{660} provides the plant with its 'clock', from which it is able to gauge the flowering season. In these short-day plants flowering may be induced when sufficient P_{660} has accumulated. That this is so is suggested by the fact that illumination during the night with light at 660 mμ (which converts P_{660} into P_{735}) inhibits flowering. How these forms of phytochrome stimulate flowering is still unsolved, but the pigment is known to be a protein, and probably acts as an enzyme which initiates the formation of some hormone or enzyme which can cause changes in the vegetative primordia (see fig. 7.8). Evidence that an enzyme or hormone-like substance is involved comes from grafting experiments, in which the leaves of one plant are treated appropriately to induce flowering and are then grafted on to an untreated plant, which then produces flowers. The surprising thing is that many different plants are capable of inducing flowering in completely different species, for instance, a treated leaf of tobacco (*Nicotiana*) can be grafted on to henbane (*Hyoscyamus niger*) and cause flower formation. This suggests that a single substance may be involved.

The changes in the apex may well be due to the action of an auxin or group of auxins similar to those discussed above. It is known that both IAA and, more particularly, the gibberellins can help to induce flowering. It may well be that the substance diffusing out of the leaves, as the result of phytochrome action, has a direct affect on the hormones of the apex, and so initiates flower development.

The system of flower induction that has been described refers to that operating in short-day plants. In long-day plants it is evident that their genetic constitution requires P_{735} to trigger off flower formation. Just how the two groups differ in their metabolism is still largely unknown (see fig. 7.7).

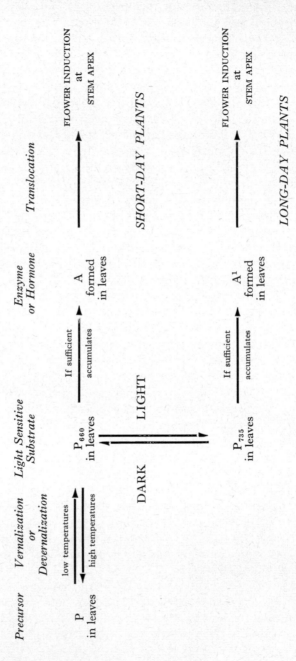

FIG. 7.8. Vernalization, day length and flower formation.

7.7 Other effects of light

The simple phototropic bending of the plant stem described above is of considerable importance to the plant, but other, less easily analysed phototropisms may be just as important. For instance, there are the movements of leaf petioles so that leaves take up a horizontal position, suitable for optimum photosynthesis, or again, there are movements which result in the leaves of a tree obtaining maximum light—producing a mosaic effect when viewed from the ground.

Finally, there are other light-induced movements, usually referred to as *photonastes*, such as the diurnal opening and closing of flowers of the daisy and the sleep-movements of leaves, as in wood-sorrel (*Oxalis acetosella*) and *Parochetus communis*. Many of these nastic movements are aided by temperature as well as light changes, though in many cases the situation is further complicated by the plants having a 'built-in' rhythm which may be slow to change even if the environmental conditions are radically altered.

Light also has important effects on seed germination. Some seeds require light to germinate, but others are inhibited to some degree by light treatment. The seeds of the purple loosestrife (*Lythrum salicaria*) and hairy willow-herb (*Epilobium hirsutum*) require light, while those of love-in-a-mist (*Nigella*) germinate best in the dark. The effect of light on seeds is, again, probably hormonal, although the full mechanism is still unknown.

7.8 The effect of gravity

Just as plant shoots bend towards the light, so roots respond to the influence of gravity and are described as positively geotropic. In many respects this tropism is similar to the phototropic response. Experiments with young roots have shown that it is usually the apex which initiates the formation of an auxin which brings about the response. The inference must be that gravity causes the accumulation of auxin at too high a concentration in the lower side of a horizontal root, thus causing *less* elongation and a consequent bending (see fig. 7.4). Alternatively, anti-auxins or growth-inhibiting substances may accumulate in the lower side. The auxin system in horizontally growing stems is complex, as there must be a balance between the geotropic and the phototropic responses. Even more complex are the changes that can occur in a single organ over the period of a few days. For instance, the flower-stalk of many species of cyclamen (e.g. *Cyclamen neapolitanum*) rises in a negatively geotropic manner until it has flowered, then it starts to curl up, exhibiting positive geotropism, and eventually more or less buries the young seed-head under the ground.

7.9 The effect of temperature

Temperature is vitally important in controlling the overall metabolic rate, different plants being adapted differently to temperature conditions, and it is one of the most important factors controlling plant distribution. The effect of temperature on germination and subsequent flowering is of particular interest. As might be expected, tropical plants germinate best at much higher temperatures than temperate plants, and their whole metabolism is 'tuned' to work best at a high temperature range. On the other hand, the cold-treatment of germinating seeds of many temperate plants

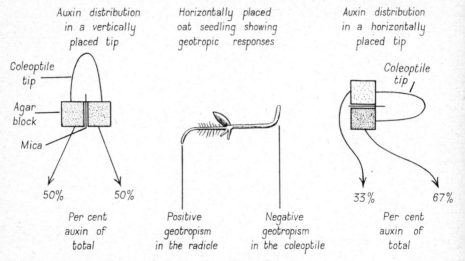

FIG. 7.9. The geotropic response. Auxin redistribution in the coleoptile. (From *Principles of Plant Physiology*, by James Bonner & Arthur W. Galston. San Francisco: W. H. Freeman Co., 1952.)

may cause them to flower earlier than usual; this effect is called *vernalization*. For instance, winter rye when germinated at 1° C. for four weeks flowered eleven weeks after planting, but seeds germinated at 18° C. produced no flower stalks in the same time (see fig. 7.10 and p. 70).

The situation is further complicated by the relationship between vernalization and day-length treatment. For instance, henbane (*Hyoscyamus niger*), normally a biennial plant, will flower only when vernalization is followed by long-day treatment, and vernalization followed by short days will not induce flowering (see figs. 7.8 and 7.11).

This is a particularly interesting case, as there also exists an annual variety of henbane, which requires no vernalization and differs from the biennial in the possession of a single dominant gene. This 'substitutes' for the cold treatment that the biennial variety requires, presumably by allowing the direct production of the light-sensitive precursor. The annual variety still requires long days to produce flowers. In other words, it is very likely that the low-temperature treatment of the seed somehow affects the hormone system of the maturing plant. It is possible that low temperatures convert a hormone precursor into an active, light-sensitive form

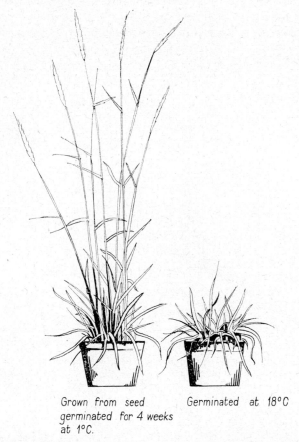

Grown from seed   Germinated at 18°C
germinated for 4 weeks
at 1°C.

FIG. 7.10. Vernalization of winter rye. Both plants 11 weeks after planting. (After Purvis (1934). *Ann. Bot., Lond.*, **48** (192) 919.)

on which the appropriate day length can act to induce flowering. Fig. 7.11 summarizes the relationship between day-length and vernalization in the biennial strain of henbane.

7.10   The role of auxins in general metabolism

It will be inferred from the examples discussed that the auxins have a vital and general role in co-ordinating plant growth. From the time the seed starts to germinate until fruit and seed are formed, the development of the plant seems for the most part to be under control of these substances. As the plant grows, the stem apex is producing hormones that make phototropic curvatures possible, but in addition the hormone production of the main apex usually has the effect of inhibiting the growth of lateral shoots, a phenomenon known as *apical dominance*. This is seen in the growth form of the pine tree, in which decapitation of the main apex will allow the lateral branches to grow much faster than before, so that one of them is

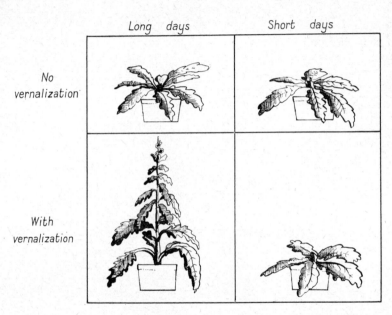

FIG. 7.11. The requirement of vernalization and long days for the flowering of the biennial strain of henbane (*Hyoscyamus niger*). (From *Principles of Plant Physiology* by James Bonner & Arthur W. Galston. San Francisco: W. H. Freeman & Co., 1952, *after* Melchers & Lang (1948) *Biol. Zentr.*, 67.)

capable of replacing the main apex. More complex changes in shape can be caused by the action of the environment on the hormone-producing system in the apex. Under temperate conditions the sumach (*Rhus*) develops as a wide-spreading shrub with branches that appear dichotomous, as the main apex often dies out. Under warmer conditions monopodial growth normally takes place and the resulting tree has a much more columnar form; this dying out of the apex may be the result of the cooler environment affecting the growth hormone system of the main apex, or it may be associated with day-length.

Just as auxins are responsible to a great extent for the general shape of the stem system, so they are responsible for the spread of the root system.

It has been known for some years that application of dilute auxins (IAA, indolylbutyric acid (IBA) and many others, though not the gibberellins) will stimulate the formation of roots by cuttings. It seems that auxin diffusing from the apex is responsible for initiating lateral root formation by stimulation of the pericycle cells. Indeed, auxins have considerable importance in initiating growth and multiplication of cells, including the initiation of thickening by causing the onset of cambial growth. Associated with this is their importance in allowing for wound healing by stimulating the division of the cells around the damaged area.

The complex processes involved in flower induction have already been discussed, but auxins are also important in inducing fruit formation. It has been realized for many years that fleshy fruits are seldom formed if fertilization has not taken place. An auxin is thought to be produced by the developing seeds that stimulates fruit formation. Some interesting results occur if unfertilized flowers are sprayed with IAA and similar auxins—fruit production without seeds may result; such 'pipless' forms may have considerable horticultural value.

Finally, auxins are important in controlling the fall of fruit and leaves. Application of auxin usually tends to delay abscission of leaf or fruit. It is thought that the auxin inhibits the enzyme system responsible for breaking down the calcium pectate of the middle lamella, which holds the cells of the separation zone together.

We see then, that the auxins are one of the chief means by which cell-to-cell co-ordination takes place. They represent a bridge between, on the one hand, the environmental factors, which to a great extent control plant development, and, on the other, the genetic constitution of the plant. The genes on the chromosomes can give only a blueprint, a potential plan, for metabolism; if the plant is incapable of reacting to its environment it will be out-competed by other better-adapted plants and will lose in the struggle for existence.

Appendix A. Experimental Procedures

An asterisk (*) indicates that the reagent is described in Appendix B.

APPENDIX TO CHAPTER 2

1. Determination of the osmotic potential of the cell sap at incipient plasmolysis
2. Determination of the water potential of the cell by the strip method
3. Determination of the water potential of the cells of bulky tissues by the weighing method
4. Determination of the effect of temperature on the permeability of the cytoplasm
5. Determination of the transpiration rate together with measurements of the environmental conditions and evaporation rate
6. The nail-varnish replica technique for examination of the leaf or stem epidermis
7. Measurement of the resistance to air flow offered by the leaf using Meidner's porometer

1. Determination of the osmotic potential of the cell sap at incipient plasmolysis (see p. 16)

Materials. Staminal hairs of *Tradescantia* and *Zebrina*; epidermal strips of leaves, especially those coloured by anthocyanins (*Rhoeo discolor*, *Tradescantia*, *Zebrina*); epidermis of red onion bulb; leaves of *Elodea* and mosses with only one cell layer.

Method. Prepare a series of solutions of sucrose of different molarities: 0·5, 0·4, 0·3, 0·2, 0·1M or higher molarities, and distilled water. Place a small piece of the tissue being examined in each of these solutions in small, covered cavity dishes.

Molarity	O.P. in Atmospheres	Molarity	O.P. in Atmospheres
0·05	1·3	0·55	16·0
0·10	2·6	0·60	17·8
0·15	4·0	0·65	19·6
0·20	5·3	0·70	21·5
0·25	6·7	0·75	23·4
0·30	8·1	0·80	25·5
0·35	9·6	0·85	27·6
0·40	11·1	0·90	29·7
0·45	12·7	0·95	32·1
0·50	14·3	1·00	34·6

Osmotic Pressures of different molarities of sucrose solutions at 20° C.
Data from Ursprung and Blum. *Ber. Deutsch. Bot. Ges.*, **34**, 525–554, 1916.
(From Meyer and Anderson's *Laboratory Plant Physiology.* © 1955, D. Van Nostrand Co., Inc., Princeton, N.J.)

Leave for twenty minutes and then mount the tissue on a slide in the same solution and cover with a cover-slip. The preparation in which about half the cells are just starting plasmolysis is regarded as at *incipient plasmolysis* and the internal and external solutions are considered isotonic.

A molar solution exerts an osmotic pressure of 22·4 atmospheres at N.T.P. provided that no ionization of the plasmolysing solution takes place. Sucrose solution, unlike potassium nitrate, is un-ionized, so no correction for ionization of the solution is needed in calculating the osmotic potential of the cell sap. The table above gives the osmotic pressure in atmospheres for different molarities of sugar solution at 20° C.

2. Determination of the water potential of the cell by the strip method (see p. 18)

Material. Thin strips of beetroot or of the corona of the daffodil.

Method. Cut the strips exactly 3 cm. long and as far as possible identical. Place these in a similar range of solutions to those described above in exp. 1, in covered Petri dishes or test-tubes. Leave for at least an hour and measure again as accurately as possible. Plot on a graph the ratio of the initial to final length, against the molarity. Estimate the water potential of the tissue, knowing that a ratio of one indicates the molarity of the cell sap. Determine the water potential in atmospheres by referring to the above table.

3. Determination of the water potential of the cells of bulky tissues by the weighing method (see p. 18)

Material. Beetroot or potato.

Method. Use a cork borer to cut discs of the material so as to produce six equivalent portions, each of about 2 gm. Dry and weigh each accurately and place separately in the range of solutions as used in exp. 1. Cover up the containers and leave for twenty-four hours. Dry quickly with blotting paper, reweigh and calculate the suction pressure as in exp. 2.

4. Determination of the effect of temperature on the permeability of the cytoplasm (see p. 18)

Material. Beetroot.

Method. Cut six slices of beetroot, 3 cm. long, 5 mm. wide and 2 mm. thick, similar as far as possible. Wash these in running water overnight and transfer them to a beaker of distilled water. Heat 200 ml. of distilled water to 75° C. and immerse one of the slices in the heated water for exactly one minute, then transfer it to a test-tube containing 10 ml. of distilled water at room temperature. As the beaker of distilled water cools repeat the procedure with a fresh slice of beetroot at 70°, 67°, 65°, 63°, 60°, 55° and 50° C. In each case place the treated slice in a separate tube of distilled water.

After half an hour shake the tubes and compare the relative amounts of red pigment (anthocyanin) that have diffused out of the slices in each case. If possible compare the colours against a colour chart or measure their density using a photoelectric colorimeter. Plot the colour density against the temperature on a

L

graph and discuss how temperature affects the permeability of the cytoplasmic membrane. What is the lowest temperature that destroys the physical nature of the cytoplasm and permits the outward diffusion of anthocyanin?

(From Meyer and Anderson's *Laboratory Plant Physiology*. © 1955, D. Van Nostrand Co., Inc., Princeton, N.J.)

5. Determination of the transpiration rate together with measurements of the environmental conditions and evaporation rate

Materials. Mesophytes e.g. dog's mercury (*Mercurialis* spp.) or hairy willow herb (*Epilobium hirsutum*) and succulents such as *Bryophyllum daigremontianum*.

Method. One of the best methods for determining the transpiration rate involves the continuous accurate weighing of a single leaf, using a torsion or other sensitive balance (see p. 21). Evaporation rates can be similarly determined using moistened filter paper.

However, the potometer and atmometer (see p. 19) may be more generally available. These can be modified for continuous operation by connecting a vertical glass tube to the end of the capillary measuring tube by means of a piece of PVC tubing. The end of this tube is dipped into a beaker of water so that the plant may transpire continuously (or the porous pot evaporate) without air being drawn into the system. A small air bubble is held in the PVC tube; this can be introduced into the capillary by squeezing the tube. Once the measurement of the rate has been taken, the bubble can be driven back into its place in the connecting tube by opening the tap on the reservoir. The usual care must be taken in setting up the apparatus to exclude leaks and air locks.

Simultaneous measurements of the temperature, light intensity† and, if necessary, wind velocity can also be taken. Ideally the rates of evaporation and transpiration per unit surface area should be calculated. The evaporating surface of the porous pot of the atmometer is easily calculated from the expression $\pi r^2 + 2\pi rh$, but to obtain the transpiring surface of the whole plant it is necessary to remove all the leaves and, by drawing their outlines on a piece of graph paper, find their total surface area. This is not quite so laborious as it sounds, as the leaves can usually be sorted into a small number of size groupings which considerably speeds up the calculation.

The various rates may be compared on a graph alongside plots for the temperature and light intensity, and conclusions can then be drawn regarding the effect of environmental conditions on the rate of transpiration.

6. The nail-varnish replica technique for examination of the leaf or stem epidermis (see p. 23)

Materials. Plants from which it is difficult or undesirable to remove the epidermis, particularly the stems of cacti and succulent plants.

Method. Paint a little clear nail-varnish on to the leaf or stem. After a few minutes remove the varnish with tweezers and mount it in water on a slide and

† For the details of the construction and calibration of a photo-voltaic light-meter see Dowdeswell, W. H., and Humby, S. R. (1953). *School Science Review*, **125**, 64.

examine under the microscope. Count the number of stomata in a given area (e.g. the low-power microscope field of view).

7. Measurement of the resistance to air flow offered by the leaf using Meidner's porometer (see p. 24)

Materials. Leaves with stomata on both surfaces work best; e.g. runner bean and sunflower.

Method. A simple porometer is illustrated in figs. A.1 and A.2. This is, in

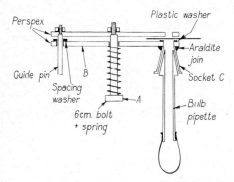

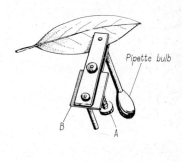

FIG. A.1. Side-view of Meidner's porometer.

FIG. A.2. Meidner's porometer attached to leaf.

The clamp can be opened to fix it to the leaf by placing the thumb on the bolt-head *A*, two fingers on the extended parts *B* of the clamp, and squeezing.

effect, a Perspex clamp which fits over the surface of the leaf. Air can be sucked through the leaf by squeezing and releasing the rubber bulb of the pipette.

First remove the pipette, then open the clamp by placing the thumb on the head of the bolt *A* and two fingers on the extended parts of the Perspex plate *B*, and then pressing. Select a suitable piece of leaf which has no large veins and release the pressure, but continue to hold the clamp.

Squeeze the rubber bulb of the pipette and then insert it into the socket *C*. Release the bulb and take the time for it to inflate. This period is proportional to the resistance of the leaf and gives a measure of the degree of opening of the stomata. Consistent results are obtained quite easily with a little practice. The airtightness of the apparatus can be checked using a microscope coverslip in lieu of the leaf.

(Adapted from Meidner (1965). *School Science Review*, No. 161, p. 149.)

APPENDIX TO CHAPTER 3

1. Identification of reducing sugars (e.g. glucose, fructose and maltose)
2. Identification of non-reducing sugars (e.g. sucrose)
3. Identification of storage polysaccharides (e.g. starch and inulin)

4. Determination of the compensation period
5. Investigation of the factors affecting the rate of photosynthesis
6. Estimation of the percentage of carbon dioxide and oxygen in a gas sample (Eggleston's method)
7. General technique of chromatography
8. Filter-paper chromatography, using long strips
9. Filter-paper chromatography, using large sheets
10. Thin-layer chromatography
11. Extraction of the photosynthetic pigments
12. Separation of the chlorophyll pigments by column chromatography
13. Setting-up and calibration of the spectrometer
14. Investigation of the fluorescence of the chlorophyll pigments
15. Investigation of the catalytic properties of extracted chloroplasts (the Hill reaction)
16. Investigation of the uptake of carbon dioxide into the leaf, using C^{14} radioactive tracer
17. Investigation of the synthesis of starch from glucose in the dark by leaves of *Pelargonium*

1. Identification of reducing sugars, e.g. the monosaccharides *glucose* and *fructose* and the disaccharide *maltose*

Materials. Most fruits, such as the apple and orange, onions, and green leaves (cleared of chlorophyll by filtration or centrifuging) (see p. 41.)

Tests. These sugars reduce the cupric ions of Fehling's†* or Benedict's†* solution to cuprous, giving a red-orange or brown precipitate on boiling. Dilute sugar solutions give only slightly yellow or greenish colours, but by careful comparison with a non-sugar-containing control solution it is usually possible to detect even small quantities of sugar. By comparison with sugar solutions of different known strengths it is also possible to obtain a rough quantitative estimate of the amount of sugar present.

This test is probably best operated on bulky tissues and extracts, but, if necessary, can also be done on a micro-scale. Sections of the material should be boiled in the reagent for a few minutes in a watch glass; grains of cuprous oxide, appearing black by transmitted light under the microscope, will appear where reducing sugars are present. It is important, though, to compare these with an unboiled control preparation.

2. Identification of non-reducing sugars, e.g. the disaccharide *sucrose*

Materials. As for reducing sugars.

Tests. This does not reduce Fehling's * or Benedict's * solution direct, and it is first necessary to hydrolyse or 'invert' the sucrose by boiling it for about a minute with dilute hydrochloric acid. This breaks the disaccharide into its two monosaccharide units, glucose and fructose. After neutralizing excess hydrochloric

---

† Note that Fehling's solution should be freshly made up from equal quantities of Fehling's A and B; Benedict's solution is used direct.

acid by adding solid sodium carbonate until effervescence ceases, Fehling's or Benedict's test can be applied as for reducing sugars.

No simple microchemical tests for sucrose are available. For the quantitative estimation of the amount of sugar present see the method of Hora, described on p. 195. A wide range of sugars may also be identified by paper chromatography, see p. 197.

3. Identification of storage polysaccharides, e.g. starch and inulin[c]

These are composed of a large number of hexose units joined together to form chains of different types. Prolonged hydrolysis may result in the formation of reducing sugars, which may be detected as above. The simpler polysaccharides are essentially food reserve substances and the more complex are important structural constituents of the cell.

(a) STARCH

Materials. Potato tubers, many rhizomes, the endosperm of seeds and photosynthesizing leaves.

Test. Starch may be identified in bulk or on a micro-scale by the use of iodine solution (dissolved in potassium iodide*), which gives a blue-black colour. During the enzymatic hydrolysis of starch (see p. 128) simpler short-chain molecules called *dextrins* may be formed, the larger of which may react with iodine to give a violet colour.

(b) INULIN

Materials. The root tubers of *Dahlia*, the stem tubers of the artichoke (*Helianthus tuberosus*), the root of the dandelion.

Test. This is a storage polysaccharide similar to starch, but it does not react with iodine and is easily recognized under the microscope by the clusters of fan-shaped crystals which appear when the tissue is dehydrated with alcohol.

4. Determination of the compensation period (see p. 39)

Material. Any small plant, e.g. wall ferns and bryophytes; single leaves of many plants; shoots of aquatic plants (e.g. *Ranunculus, Elodea, Callitriche*).

Method. Place a filter-paper in the bottom of a small deep glass dish and moisten it with distilled water. Place a cavity block on the filter-paper and fill it with 1 ml. sodium bicarbonate indicator solution.* This solution tends to equilibrate its carbon dioxide content with that of the atmosphere, and should previously have been aspirated through with atmospheric air until it is a red colour. Arrange the plant material, which should have a minimum of soil, around the cavity block and seal the dish with a vaselined piece of glass (see fig. A.3). Single leaves may be arranged as shown in fig. A.4, alternatively water plants may be placed direct in the indicator solution and the tube sealed.

Keep the dish or tube in a dark room at a fixed temperature for about ten hours so that respiration alone can take place, and then transfer it to bright illumination. Take care not to warm the plant with the illuminating lamps and keep it at the same temperature throughout the experiment. The compensation period is given by the time taken for the indicator to change back from yellow to the original red colour. The experiment may be repeated at different temperatures and at different light intensities.

Modified after Hosokawa & Odani (1957). Compensation period and vertical ranges of epiphtes. *Journal of Ecology*, **45**, No. 3, p. 901.

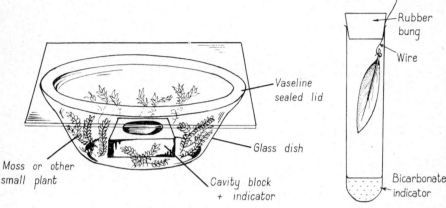

Fig. A.3. Jar system used for determining the compensation period of small plants.

Fig. A.4. Simple tube for determining the compensation period of a single leaf.

5. Investigation of factors affecting rate of photosynthesis. (see p. 42).

Material. Young sprigs of *Elodea canadensis*.

Method. Place a few short sprigs of *Elodea* in a 1-litre beaker, preferably containing the water in which the plant was growing. Illuminate brightly for about half an hour. At the end of this period a stream of bubbles should be coming from the cut ends of the shoots. The number of bubbles produced per minute gives a measure of the rate of photosynthesis. The percentage oxygen in the gas evolved can be estimated if required (see exp. 6 below). Take care not to move the beaker or sprigs of *Elodea* during the course of the experiment and also give the material time to settle down when alterations are made to the conditions. It may be useful to use a piece of glass as a heat filter between the bulb and the beaker. The distance (d) between the bulb and the *Elodea* should be measured as accurately as possible from the front of the bulb to the centre of the photosynthetic area of the *Elodea*. The rate of bubbling will differ from shoot to shoot, so once a shoot has been selected it alone should be used throughout the experiment.

(a) To determine the effect of light intensity on the rate of photosynthesis

Vary the light intensity by moving a bright lamp progressively nearer the *Elodea*. Knowing that the light intensity at distance d from the lamp is proportional to $1/d^2$, plot $1/d^2$ against the amount of oxygen produced. Where the graph is a straight line, light is controlling the rate of the reaction, but if the rate of photosynthesis tends to show no further increase as the higher intensities are approached, then some other factor, possibly temperature or carbon dioxide availability, is limiting the rate of the reaction.

(*b*) To determine the effect of temperature on the rate of photosynthesis

Set up the apparatus as in the previous experiment, but keep the light intensity constant, first, at a low intensity and then at a high intensity. Record the rate of photosynthesis in each case at 18° and 28° C. Under high illumination light is not limiting the rate of the process, and a rise in temperature of 10° may double the rate of the reaction ($Q_{10} = 2$). Under low illumination a similar rise in temperature makes little difference to the rate of photosynthesis. This indicates that there is a distinct purely chemical stage in photosynthesis in addition to a photochemical stage.

6. Estimation of the percentage of carbon dioxide and oxygen in a gas sample (Eggleston's method)

The apparatus is a simple capillary tube to which is attached a brass screw; this should be carefully greased to prevent a leak (fig. A.5). Turning the screw allows for a gas sample to be taken in or out of the tube.

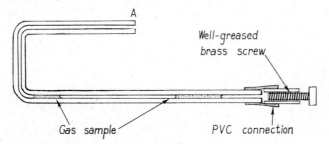

Fig. A.5. Eggleston's capillary device for gas analysis. (Note: the long arm of the capillary should be 30 cm. in length.)

First turn the screw fully in, dip the end of the capillary (A) in water and un-screw until about a 5-cm. length of water has been taken up. To take up a gas sample, adjust the water column in the capillary so that it reaches the open end, then place the end in the atmosphere to be sampled and unscrew until about a 10-cm. length of gas has been drawn in. Seal this by drawing in a little more water. Place the tube on its side in a water-bath to bring it to a uniform tempera-ture. Taking care not to warm the capillary tube with your hands, measure the length of the gas sample. Then place the open end in a strong solution of potas-sium hydroxide to absorb the carbon dioxide. Screw in until the gas bubble is almost at the end of the capillary. Unscrew and draw in a little of the reagent. Using the screw, shunt the gas sample backwards and forwards to allow it to come into contact with the potassium hydroxide. Leave to stand for five minutes and then measure the length of the bubble as before. Any shortening indicates how much carbon dioxide was present.

The last stage is then repeated using alkaline pyrogallol* to absorb the oxygen. It is always necessary to estimate the carbon dioxide separately, as the pyrogallol absorbs both oxygen and carbon dioxide. At the end of each run rinse the tubes in dilute acid to remove all traces of the alkaline reagent. Take care with these reagents as they are all caustic and can cause burns and damage clothes.

(Adapted from *Biology Students' text*, Year III, of the Nuffield Foundation Science Teaching project.)

7. General technique of chromatography

Chromatography is used for separating and identifying unknown mixtures of closely related organic and inorganic substances.

Most chromatographic apparatus consists of some solid medium or *adsorbing substance*. This is arranged over a solvent, usually composed of two or more substances, which can pass through the adsorbant. A mixture of the substances to be separated is placed on the adsorbant so that, as the solvent passes through them, they may be drawn along too. Separation of the substances in the mixture takes place if some of them are more strongly adsorbed than others. The *partition effect* is usually also important as the substances will assort themselves on the chromatogram according to their partition coefficients in the solvents.

Ideally the position reached by any particular substance should always be the same under identical conditions, and so it is possible to identify the substances formed. In practice though a good deal of care is needed if reproducible results are to be obtained.

A number of different chromatographic techniques are useful in biology. The simplest is perhaps *filter-paper chromatography*, using long strips or large sheets. There is also *thin-layer chromatography* which uses thin layers of silica-gel mixed with plaster of Paris on glass plates. These two techniques are useful for identifying mixtures of substances. Filter-paper techniques are probably better when plenty of time is available, but thin-layer methods are particularly useful as good separations can be obtained in under an hour. *Column chromatography* is used to separate mixtures in solution and is carried out in a tall glass column filled with cellulose.

Each of these techniques is described below; a full table of substances, methods of extraction from plant material, solvents, developing sprays and R_f values is given on p. 164.

8. Filter-paper chromatography using long strips

The chromatogram jar (see fig. 3.14)

Fit a tall narrow glass jar (about 45 cm. high) with a cork that has been bored to take a glass rod fitted with a small hook at its end. This glass rod should be able to slip up and down in the cork. Place 2 cm. of the solvent (see p. 164) in the jar and cut a long strip of Whatman No. 1 filter-paper (it can be obtained in a roll of the required width). Solvents run at rates which change with different papers and according to the way the paper is hung. The box containing the filter-paper is normally marked to indicate the way the solvent should flow. Arrange the glass rod and filter-paper strip so that the filter paper can hang freely in the air without touching the solvent.

Loading the paper

Mark in pencil a spot 3 cm. from the base of the paper strip and load the unknown, or known, comparison substance carefully on to the spot, using a fine capillary or fine wire loop. It is important to load plenty of material (unless it is a concentrated solution of a single known substance), but it is also important to keep the spot less than 0·5 cm. diameter.

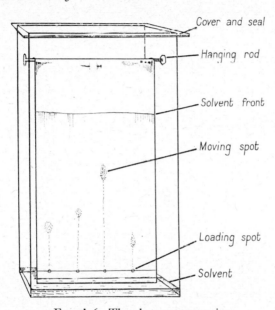

Fig. A.6. The chromatogram jar.

Running the chromatogram

Attach the loaded filter-paper to the hook by means of a paper-clip. Place it in the jar for ten minutes for the atmosphere inside the jar to equilibrate. Then lower the glass rod so that the paper dips 0·5 cm. into the solvent. Make sure that the cork is a proper seal, if necessary smear a little Vaseline around it and the rod. The solvent will rise slowly up the paper, carrying the material from the spot with it. When the solvent has risen about 30 cm. up the paper it can be removed. Mark the height that the solvent has reached (the solvent front).

Development of the chromatogram

Dry the paper carefully, preferably in a fume cupboard. Remember that many solvents are inflammable or noxious. Some spots will be coloured already, others need a developing spray. Mark the spots as they appear and make a note

Table of Chromatographic Techniques

Substances	Solvents
Chlorophyll and Carotenoid pigments	*Using thin-layer or filter-paper chromatography* 100 parts petroleum ether (B.P. 100°–120° C.), 12 parts pure acetone. The solvent listed below gives a better separation with thin-layer chromatograms. *Using thin-layer or column chromatography* (for rest of details of column chromatography see p. 170) 100 parts petroleum ether (B.P. 60°–80° C.), 20 parts pure acetone.
Plant acids	100 parts *n*-butyl formate, 40 parts 98 per cent formic acid, 10 parts distilled water. *Take care with these substances.* Add 0·5 gm. sodium formate to each 100 ml. of solvent and sufficient solid bromophenol blue to turn the solvent a pale orange colour.
Amino-acids Sugars and Plant acids	Phenol-water Take 28 gm. of pure crystalline phenol, which should be white and unoxidized. *Take care when handling this substance; it is preferable to use rubber gloves.* Place the phenol in a stoppered separating funnel and add 12 ml. of distilled water. This is the minimum quantity for work with a filter-paper strip, use a larger quantity if necessary. Add a little more sodium chloride and shake thoroughly. Fill the funnel with coal gas to prevent oxidation and leave until the layers separate out, which usually takes at least an hour. The lower layer is the phenol saturated with water; reject the upper layer.
Amino-acids and Sugars	120 parts *n*-butanol, 30 parts glacial acetic acid, 60 parts distilled water.
Amino-acids	*Using two-way filter-paper chromatography* This system gives a more effective separation. After running the chromatogram in either of the above two solvents, dry it but do not develop it. Turn the paper on edge and run it in the following solvent: 180 parts ethanol, 10 parts ammonium hydroxide, 10 parts distilled water.
Anthocyanin pigments	40 parts *n*-butanol, 10 parts glacial acetic acid, 50 parts distilled water. Make up the solvent in a separating funnel. The lower layer is the required solvent, reject the upper layer.

Table of Chromatographic Techniques (*continued*)

Substances	Methods of Extraction from Plant material	Development
Chlorophyll and Carotenoid pigments	Grind in pure acetone or as described on on p. 169	No development necessary. Ultra-violet light is particularly useful for viewing spots.
	,,	,,
Plant acids	Grind in 70 per cent ethanol	Dry the chromatogram carefully, preferably in a fume cupboard. Sometimes further development is worthwhile by holding the chromatogram over a bottle of ammonium hydroxide. Do not let the chromatogram get too blue. The spots sometimes become clearer if the chromatogram is left for some days.
Amino-acids	Grind in water or 80 per cent ethanol	Dry the chromatogram carefully, preferably in a fume cupboard as phenol fumes are noxious. Spray with 2 per cent ninhydrin in *n*-butanol. (Care: ninhydrin is a carcinogen.) Heat the chromatogram strongly for the spots to appear.
Sugars	Grind in 50 per cent ethanol	Dry the chromatogram carefully, preferably in a fume cupboard as phenol fumes are noxious. Spray with either a 3 per cent solution of *para*-anisidine hydrochloride in *n*-butanol plus a few drops hydrochloric acid or with 10 per cent solution of resorcinol in acetone plus a few drops hydrochloric acid.
Plant acids	Grind in water	Dry the chromatogram carefully, preferably in a fume cupboard as phenol fumes are noxious. Spray with bromothymol blue adjusted to pH 8·5 with sodium hydroxide.
Amino-acids	Grind in water or 80 per cent ethanol	Dry the chromatogram carefully (butanol is highly inflammable) spray with 2 per cent ninhydrin in *n*-butanol. (Care: ninhydrin is a carcinogen.) Heat the chromatogram strongly for the spots to appear.
Sugars	Grind in 0·1M sodium acetate in water	Dry the chromatogram carefully (butanol is highly inflammable) spray with either a 3 per cent solution of *para*-anisidine hydrochloride in *n*-butanol plus a few drops hydrochloric acid. Heat the chromatogram strongly for the spots to appear.
Amino-acids	(as above)	Dry the chromatogram carefully (ethanol is highly inflammable). Spray with 2 per cent ninhydrin in *n*-butanol. Heat the chromatogram strongly for the spots to appear.
Anthocyanin pigments	Grind in 80 per cent ethanol	No development necessary. Treatment with ammonia vapour makes the spots blue and sometimes intensifies them.

Table of R_f Values

| Substances | Identification of Spots | | | | | |
| | Thin-layer Chromatography | | | Filter-paper Chromatography | | |
	Substance	R_f value	Colour	Substance	R_f value	Colour
Chlorophyll and Carotenoid pigments	Chlorophyll b	0·10	Yellow-green	Chlorophyll b	0·45	Green
	Chlorophyll a	0·11	Blue-green	Chlorophyll a	0·65	Blue-green
	Xanthophyll	0·22	Yellow	Xanthophyll	0·71	Yellow-brown
	Phaeophytin	0·28	Grey	Phaeophytin	0·83	Grey
	Carotene	0·90	Yellow	Carotene	0·95	Yellow
	Chlorophyll b	0·17	Yellow-green			
	Xanthophyll (?)	0·19	Yellow			
	Chlorophyll a	0·23	Blue-green			
	Xanthophyll	0·35	Yellow			
	Phaeophytin	0·44	Grey			
	Carotene	0·96	Yellow			
Plant acids	Tartaric acid	0·32	Yellow against	Tartaric acid	0·20	Yellow against
	Citric acid	0·50	a purple back-	Citric acid	0·25	a purple back-
	Malic acid	0·61	ground	Oxalic acid	0·32	ground
	Pyruvic acid	0·85		Malic acid	0·37	
	Succinic acid	0·92		Succinic acid	0·57	
Amino-acids	Glycine	0·29	Orange-red	Glutamic acid	0·38	Orange-red
	Arginine	0·32	Deep red-purple	Glycine	0·50	Brown-purple
				Tyrosine	0·66	Deep purple
	Cystine	0·32	Pink	Arginine	0·70	Red-purple
	Valine	0·41	Red-purple	Alanine	0·72	Blue-purple
	Phenylalanine	0·52	Brown	Leucine	0·91	Deep purple
				Proline	0·95	Yellow
Sugars				Glucose	0·31	Red with re-sorcinol, yel-low – brown with anisidine
				Sucrose	0·35	
				Fructose	0·46	
Plant acids				Tartaric acid	0·23	Yellow against
				Citric acid	0·32	a blue back-
				Oxalic acid	0·35	ground
				Malic acid	0·43	
				Pyruvic acid	0·59	
				Succinic acid	0·60	
Amino-acids	Glycine	0·20	Orange-red			
	Arginine	0·23	Deep red-purple			
	Tyrosine	0·25	Purple			
	Cystine	0·26	Pink			
	Valine	0·39	Red-purple			
Sugars	Sucrose	0·24	Yellow-brown			
	Fructose	0·31	Yellow-brown			
	Glucose	0·43	Yellow-brown			
Amino-acids	—			—		
Anthocyanin pigments				Delphinidin	0·59	Blue-purple
				Pelargonidin	0·73	Bright red
				Peonidin	0·74	Magenta
				Cyanidin	0·79	Mauve-purple

of their colour as they often fade quickly. It is also often worth while to view the chromatogram in ultra-violet light (see p. 171).

Identification of the products

Identification of the spots is possible by running a parallel chromatogram alongside that with the unknown substances. This chromatogram is loaded with a known substance that is thought to be present in the unknown mixture. The resulting chromatograms are then compared and the R_f values of the spots calculated:

$$R_f = \frac{\text{Distance moved by solute spot}}{\text{Distance moved by solvent front}}$$

In addition, R_f values can be found in tables, but it must be emphasized that it is almost always necessary to run a comparison chromatogram with a known substance before a certain identification can be made.

It is also possible to make a rough assessment of the comparative amounts of the substances in the mixture by comparing the size and density of the various spots.

9. Filter-paper chromatography using large sheets

Fit a large glass jar (e.g. an old battery jar) with a cover as shown in fig. A.6. Arrange the glass rod so that the filter-paper sheet can hang to the bottom of the jar. Load the substances on to the paper as described above. Put about 2 cm. of solvent in the bottom of the jar and also stick a few filter-papers, moistened with solvent, to the side of the jar and dipping in the solvent. This helps to keep the atmosphere inside the tank saturated with solvent vapour. Lower the paper in carefully and fix it to the glass rod with a clip or pin. Seal the jar as quickly as possible after smearing Vaseline around the rim or by using a strip of Plasticine around the edge.

Comparison of known and unknown spots is much easier than with the thin strips described above.

If a square tank is used, *two-way chromatograms* can be made by running the chromatogram as described and then using a new solvent and turning the paper on edge (see p. 164).

10. Thin-layer chromatography

Preparation of the glass plates

Old half-plate photographic plates, carefully cleaned in chromic acid, make very suitable thin-layer plates. Arrange about twelve of these along a flat bench as shown in fig. A.7.

The plates should be arranged side-by-side with their long sides touching. Clamp a ruler at one end so that the plates cannot slip. Then stick Sellotape along the two outer edges of the plates. This prevents the plates from slipping and also keeps the roller at exactly the right height above the plates.

Take 30 gm. of the adsorbant (Kieselgel G after Stahl), and add it to 60 ml. of distilled water, stirring quickly and thoroughly. Pour the Kieselgel on to one end of the plates and spread it with a glass roller, moving the roller steadily and evenly across the plates. *Never move it more than once.* Take care to keep sufficient Kieselgel in front of the roller. Leave the plates to dry for one hour, then remove the Sellotape and incubate them at between 80° and 100° C for one hour. The plates may then be kept in a desiccator for a few days until they are needed.

Before the plates are used clean off any traces of Sellotape and also scrape a 1-cm. band of Kieselgel from the vertical edges of the plate (see fig. A.8), this prevents 'billowing' of the solvent as it comes into contact with the edges of the plate. Handle the plate at the edges only, never touch the Kieselgel.

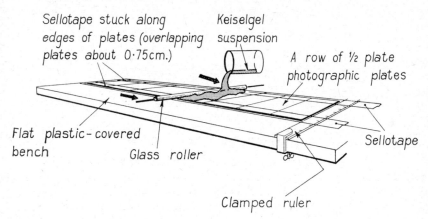

FIG. A.7. Spreading thin-layer chromatogram plates. (From Baron, W. M. M. (1964). *School Science Review*, No. 158, p. 62.)

Loading the chromatogram

Spots of known or unknown substances should be applied about 1 cm. from the lower end of the Kieselgel. Spots *must be small*, 2–3 mm. is quite large enough. Use a minute wire loop for loading, as this causes less damage to the Kieselgel than a capillary. Only one application of concentrated known substances is usually needed, but considerably more material of unknown and usually dilute mixtures will have to be added. Use scratched marks at the top of the plate to label the spots.

Running the chromatogram

Sufficient solvent is prepared to fill the chromatogram jar about 1·5 cm. deep. In this way it will come into proper contact with the Kieselgel without washing away the loaded spots. The most suitable jars are probably the small glass jars, complete with ground glass covers that are often used for museum specimens. These will take two plates at a time and about 60 ml. of solvent is usually sufficient. After placing the solvent in the jar keep the top on for a few minutes to allow the solvent and its vapour to come into equilibrium. Added saturation of the tank atmosphere can be obtained by coating the sides of the tank with filter-paper, dipping in the solvent. Then carefully put the plate in and replace the cover and seal the jar with a Plasticine strip or Vaseline. Ether-containing solvents usually take about twenty-five minutes to run. Phenol will take about an hour. Remove the plate when the solvent front has risen to 10 cm.

Identification of the products

The spots may be identified from R_f values; the main problem is, however, that owing to lack of uniformness in the Kieselgel layer, exactly comparable

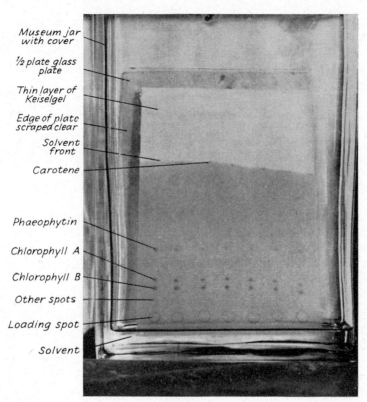

Museum jar with cover
½ plate glass plate
Thin layer of Keiselgel
Edge of plate scraped clear
Solvent front
Carotene
Phaeophytin
Chlorophyll A
Chlorophyll B
Other spots
Loading spot
Solvent

FIG. A.8. A thin-layer chromatogram plate separating the chlorophyll pigments. (From Baron, W. M. M. (1964). *School Science Review*, No. 158, p. 62.)

R_f values are seldom obtained. This can be overcome by using known substances for comparison or by comparing with a standard dye range. A mixture of two dyes (Sudan Red G and Indophenol) can be used as a control with some solvents.

11. Extraction of the photosynthetic pigments (see p. 52)

Materials. Leaves of the nettle (*Urtica dioica*).

Method. Take a few leafy stems and kill them by immersion for a few seconds in boiling water. Shake the leaves free of water, place them in a mortar with about 30 ml. of pure acetone and grind to extract the pigments. Alternatively,

dried nettle leaves may be ground up with acetone direct. Filter the extract
through glass wool, using a Büchner funnel, and place the filtrate in a separating
funnel. Add an equal volume of petroleum ether (B.P. 100°–120°C) and shake
the mixture. Wash the extract three times with distilled water, rejecting the watery
layer each time. Add solid sodium sulphate to help break the emulsion down and
let the solution stand for some minutes over sodium sulphate, it is then ready
for use.

12. Separation of the chlorophyll pigments by column chromatography
(see p. 52)

Material. Freshly made extract of the pigments.

Method. Fill a 30 cm., 1-cm. bore glass tube with pure Whatman cellulose
powder, a small piece of glass wool being used as a pad at the lower end (see fig.
3.15). It is important to take care with this loading, only a little cellulose being
added at a time and a glass ramrod being used to firm it between each addition.
Then wash the column through with a mixture of 100 parts petroleum ether
(B.P. 60°–80° C) to 20 parts pure acetone, using a filter pump to help draw the
mixture through; the column is then ready for use. Add 5 ml. of the chlorophyll
extract to the top of the column and allow it to sink into the cellulose. Set up a
dropping funnel filled with solvent over the column, adjust it to drip steadily
and the pigments will be washed down the column. The pigments can be seen
to separate in the column as they are washed down, the least adsorbed substances
travelling most quickly. After a few minutes the carotene solution will begin to
drip out of the column; collect it and the remaining pigments (in the order:
carotene, phaeophytin, xanthophyll, chlorophyll *a* and chlorophyll *b*) in a series
of test-tubes held under the column. (Adapted from Baron (1960). *School
Science Review*, No. 145, p. 93.)

13. Setting-up and calibration of the spectrometer (see p. 54)

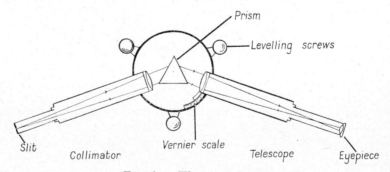

FIG. A.9. The spectrometer.

If a wavelength or constant-deviation spectrometer is not available the ordinary spectrometer can be calibrated so that the wavelengths of absorption and
emission bands can be measured.

It is first necessary to set up the apparatus so as to obtain maximum resolution and the desired dispersion of the spectrum. First focus the cross-lines by adjusting the telescope eyepiece (see fig. A.9), then focus the telescope on a distant object. Bring the telescope into line with the collimator and illuminate the latter. Adjust the position of the collimator slit in or out until a sharp image of the slit is formed in the plane of the eyepiece cross-lines. Place the prism as shown in the diagram (fig. A.9), clamp it down and place a black cloth over the central part of the apparatus. By rotating the eyepiece telescope different parts of the spectrum can be viewed and the angles on the vernier scale noted.

The light produced by a mercury vacuum tube or arc is most useful for calibration, as it produces a series of sharp emission bands, the wavelengths of which are known and can be compared with the angle on the vernier scale.

MERCURY VAPOUR SPECTRUM	
Wavelength (mμ)	*Colour*
576·96	Yellow
579·07	Yellow
546·07	Green
435·82	Violet

Fainter lines are also visible at: 623·2, 615·2, 495·97, 491·64, 407·81, 404·68, 365·0, 313·1 and 312·6 mμ.

Plot the angles and wavelengths on a graph so that any intermediate wavelengths may subsequently be determined from the curve obtained.

Measurement of the wavelengths of absorption and emission spectra is much simpler using the Hilger's wavelength spectrometer. Here the collimator and telescope are fixed, and as the prism is rotated the different parts of the spectrum are visible and their respective wavelengths can be read off directly on the drum. It is, however, wise to check the apparatus before use, and this is most simply done by examining the sodium flame, which has two close orange emission bands at 589·0 and 589·59 mμ.

14. Investigation of the fluorescence of the chlorophyll pigments (see p. 55)

Materials. Fresh leaves of lesser celandine (*Ranunculus ficaria*), fresh or dried leaves of nettle (*Urtica dioica*).

Method. Grind up a small quantity of the leaves in acetone and centrifuge the extract. Examine in ultra-violet light; a strong red fluorescence should be seen.

A note on the ultra-violet light source

A useful ultra-violet lamp can be obtained for about £3. It is a 125-watt special blue bulb, but requires a choke, capacitor and special three-contact lampholder. The wavelengths of ultra-violet light emitted by this lamp should not cause damage to the retina of the eye, during short exposures, but, on the other hand, the lamp cannot be used for any sterilization procedures. The lamp should be allowed to warm up for several minutes before use.

M

15. Investigation of the catalytic properties of extracted chloroplasts (the Hill reaction) (see p. 56)

Material. Fresh leaves of spinach.

Method. Prepare 40 ml. M/15-phosphate buffer pH 6·5 (see p. 205). Cool this by immersing the flask in a freezing mixture and at the same time cool a pestle and mortar. Chop up some fresh spinach leaves into the mortar and then grind them to extract the chloroplasts in about 10 ml. of ice-cold phosphate buffer. Centrifuge at medium speed for three minutes to throw down cell-wall detritus and starch grains. The centrifuge should be arranged so that the large tubes contain freezing mixture, and these hold smaller, inner tubes containing the chloroplast extract. Decant the chloroplast suspension into clean centrifuge tubes and recentrifuge at high speed for ten minutes. Reject the supernatant and resuspend the chloroplasts in 4 ml. ice-cold buffer.

Prepare eight small-sized test-tubes as follows, *taking care with the solution of potassium cyanide*:

1,2	1 ml. very dilute aqueous 2 : 6 dichlorophenol-indophenol	0·5 ml., M/2-KCl	0·5 ml. chloroplast suspension
3,4	1 ml. very dilute aqueous 2 : 6 dichlorophenol-indophenol	0·5 ml., M/2-KCl	0.5 ml. boiled chloroplast suspension (control)
5,6	1 ml. very dilute aqueous 2 : 6 dichlorophenol-indophenol	0·5 ml., M/2-KCl	0·5 ml. chloroplast suspension + 2 drops M/1,000-KCN
7,8	no dye (control)	0·5 ml., M/2-KCl	0·5 ml. chloroplast suspension

Add the purified chloroplast extract to each tube, except 3 and 4, to which are added boiled chloroplast extract. Illuminate tubes 1, 3, 5 and 7 brightly and leave the other tubes in the dark. Take the time for the dye to bleach in the light-treated tubes. Compare the colours with those that have been in the dark. What conclusions can you draw about the reducing properties of illuminated chloroplasts?

16. Investigation of the uptake of carbon dioxide into the leaf using C^{14} radioactive tracer (see p. 43)

Material. Small, actively growing shoots of many plants such as tomato or *Zebrina* (*Tradescantia*). Variegated plants could also be used. These shoots need not be rooted.

Method.

1. *Apparatus.* Set up the apparatus shown in fig. A.10. This consists of a dropping funnel about 10 cm. long, fitted with a rubber bung, tube and tap. The funnel is arranged to contain two specimen tubes resting on a piece of pierced expanded polystyrene. The smaller tube contains the tracer solution; the larger contains water and the shoot, some leaves of which should be covered with black polythene, others with transparent polythene, using a paper clip.

The dropping tube leads directly into a wash-bottle containing a strong solution of potassium hydroxide. This is connected to a second similar bottle and finally to a third which should contain water. At the end of the experiment the tube from this bottle is connected to a filter pump.

A 100-watt bulb is arranged about 30 cm. from the tube, with a sheet of glass in between to prevent heating, and the whole apparatus is placed in a fume cupboard. The bench should be covered with a sheet of tarred paper in case of spills. Make sure that there are no leaks in the apparatus.

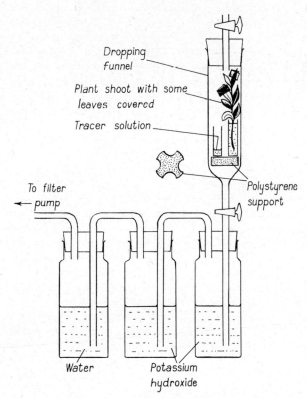

FIG. A.10. Apparatus used for investigating the uptake of $C^{14}O_2$ into the plant (see p. 46).

2. *Tracer technique.* When the apparatus is set up, carefully remove the calculated quantity of the solution of radioactive tracer from the phial or serum bottle and place it in the smaller specimen tube. This will probably be only a few drops. Use a disposable syringe or special pipette fitted with a rubber bulb; *under no circumstances use a mouth pipette.* Wear rubber gloves throughout the experiment. Carry out this operation on an enamel tray in the fume cupboard. The C^{14} is usually obtained in the form of a solution of sodium carbonate and the quantity required must be calculated so as to give a strength of 10 μc (microcuries) in the apparatus. C^{14} is a weak β-emitter (0·155 MeV) and needs a

sensitive Geiger–Muller (GM) tube for proper detection and counting (e.g. Mullard MX 168 or, better, MX 168/01).

Place the specimen tube in a deep freeze or freezing mixture until the carbonate solution is frozen, taking precautions to ensure that the tube is not knocked over. Note that solutions of radioactive sodium carbonate should not be left for long exposed to the atmosphere, as gaseous exchange takes place; accordingly keep all such solutions properly stoppered.

When the carbonate is frozen place a few crystals of solid sodium bisulphate on the surface of the carbonate. Place the tube in the dropping funnel, put in the rubber bung and close the top tap, but leave the lower open. The filter pump should *not* be on at this stage. Turn on the lamp; as the carbonate thaws it reacts with the bisulphate and the radioactive carbon dioxide is evolved. After half an hour close the lower tap and leave the apparatus with the light on for between 12 and 24 hours. Finally, open the lower tap, turn on the filter pump and then open the upper tap. Draw air through the apparatus for at least half an hour to remove the radioactive carbon dioxide. Then carefully remove the rubber bung and check for radiation; if necessary continue to draw air through the apparatus for a further period. When there is little carbon dioxide left, take out the plant material and cut off the wet parts of the shoot, put these in the waste bottle (see below).

3. *Autoradiographic technique.* This is used to investigate the sites of absorption of the radioactive carbon dioxide. Place the shoots on a piece of paper, 16×12 cm., carefully separate out the leaves (still using rubber gloves) and stick the shoots down to the paper, using sticky tape. Make a note to show where the leaves were covered and remove the clips and covers. Place the paper in a thin plastic bag to prevent any radioactive plant juices contaminating the film or holder. Take the material to the dark-room and place it in a special half-plate X-ray exposure film holder. Arrange the material so that the emulsion surface of the X-ray film is facing the underneath of the paper to which the plant is stuck. There will then be a sheet of plastic and paper between the film and the plant but no pieces of tape. Close up the film holder and leave for between 36 and 48 hours. Do not press the material too hard in the folder if the shoots are full of sap.

Suitable X-ray films are Kodak *Kodirex* and *Crystallex*. The former is the faster and is probably the more satisfactory film, though the latter gives a very clear print. Deep-red safe lights may be used for loading and development, though Kodak recommend *Wratten* 6B (brown). After exposure remove the film from the folder and develop it in Kodak D-19b for 5–12 minutes at 20° C. Fix in Kodak *Unifix*.

Compare the autoradiographs with the sketches showing which leaves were covered. Mark the autoradiographs accordingly and make what deductions you can about the sites of absorption of the carbon dioxide.

4. *Identification of the substances formed using autoradiography of chromatograms.* Remove the plant shoots from the paper backing and place them in a beaker containing a small quantity of 90 per cent ethanol. Use the minimum quantity to cover the plant. Cover with a watch glass and heat the beaker on a water-bath in a fume cupboard for ten minutes.

Spot the solution on to three or more sheets of filter paper for chromatography (see p. 167). Run the chromatograms in *n*-butanol or other solvents. Spray with appropriate reagents to identify amino-acids, sugars and plant acids. After marking and identifying the spots make a rough estimate of the distribution of tracer, using a scaler, and make a note of the readings from the various spots. Finally, cover the chromatograms with plastic (both sides) and set them up in

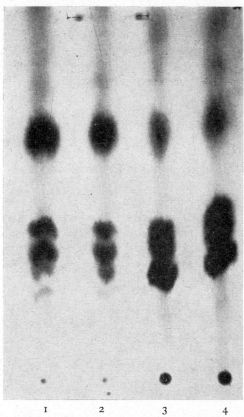

FIG. A.11. Autoradiograph of chromatogram of extracts of tomato (1 and 2) and *Zebrina* (3 and 4) after the plants had been allowed to photosynthesise in an atmosphere containing $C^{14}O_2$. (Chromatographic solvent: *n*-butanol, acetic acid water. Fourteen days' exposure on Kodirex.)

the dark-room with X-ray film in the usual way. Leave for 14 days and then develop the films. Compare the autoradiographs and chromatograms carefully and deduce which substances have accumulated tracer from the radioactive carbon dioxide. An example of such an autoradiograph is illustrated in fig. A.11.

5. *Washing and disposal of waste.* C^{14} has a long half-life (5568 years), so special care is necessary in handling it and in the disposal of waste. At the conclusion of the experiment wash the glassware, dropping funnel and rubber bung

with dilute potassium hydroxide, transferring the washings and all the radioactive liquids (from the wash bottles and specimen tubes) to a specially-labelled, large-stoppered waste jar. A second washing of the contaminated glassware should be carried out, using a little warm brine and detergent; these washings should also be regarded as 'hot' and put into the waste jar. Once the contamination has been removed the glassware may have a final wash in warm water and detergent. Dry the apparatus with tissue and keep it solely for this work. The use of special warning tape is useful here and throughout the experiment. Any solid wastes (e.g. plant material) should be kept in a separate bottle. Regulations for the disposal of wastes are strict. Full details of various techniques are given in Faires, R. A., and Parkes, B. H. (1958) *Radioisotope Laboratory techniques*; Newnes, London. The reader in the United Kingdom is also advised to consult the Administrative Memorandum 1/65 of the Dept. of Education and Science, Curzon Street, London, W.1, which gives further details and regulations for the use of radioactive materials in schools. Permission to use radioactive materials in schools must also first be obtained from the department. Radioactive materials may be obtained from The Radiochemical Centre, Amersham, Bucks.

17. Investigation of the synthesis of starch from glucose in the dark by leaves of Pelargonium (see p. 58)

Material. Young leaves of *Pelargonium*, or tobacco.

Method. Sterilize two small, but deep Pyrex dishes together with suitable glass covers. Sterilize 20 ml., 5 per cent glucose solution and pour it into one dish, pour 20 ml. sterile distilled water into the other (as a control). Using a cork borer, cut several 1-cm.-diameter discs from a leaf of a *Pelargonium* plant that has been in the dark for at least twenty-four hours and sterilize them by shaking for three minutes in 1 per cent sodium hypochlorite solution. Wash them in sterile distilled water and float one in each dish. Label the dishes and leave them in the dark for three days. Finally, take them out and mark the leaf disc that has been in the glucose by cutting out a small nick. Remove the chlorophyll by boiling in 90 per cent alcohol for some minutes and test with iodine for starch formation.

APPENDIX TO CHAPTER 4

1. Investigation of the rate of respiration by the Pettenkofer technique
2. Determination of the respiratory quotient (RQ) by means of the Ganong respirometer
3. The Warburg manometric technique
4. Determination of the respiratory quotient by Warburg manometry
5. Investigation of the effect of addition of the inhibitor KCN on the rate respiration
6. Calculation of the flask constants of the Warburg manometer
7. Identification of acetaldehyde as an intermediate in anaerobic respiration

8. Identification of some plant acids by simple chemical tests
9. Identification of plant acids by chromatography
10. Investigation of polyphenol oxidase as an example of a terminal oxidase
11. Investigation of the dehydrogenase activity of etiolated pea shoots
12. Spectroscopic examination of the cytochromes

1. Investigation of the rate of respiration by the Pettenkofer technique
(see p. 64)

Materials. Germinating seeds at various stages, ripening fruits, etc.
Method. APPARATUS.
Set up the apparatus shown in the diagram fig. 4.2, this consists of seven main pieces:

1. A small piston-action blowing motor.
2. A tower containing moist soda-lime to absorb carbon dioxide. (Soda-lime is a mixture of sodium hydroxide and calcium oxide.)
3. A pressure control unit consisting of a capillary tube which can slide up and down inside a boiling-tube. Raising or lowering the capillary tube will control the rate of flow of gas through the apparatus.
4. A check-flask which contains calcium hydroxide; if this goes cloudy the soda-lime tower must be renewed immediately.
5. A respiration chamber, the size of which will depend on the material being investigated. For small amounts a bottle or gas jar can be used, for larger specimens an old battery jar can be satisfactorily modified. The chamber should be covered in black paper to prevent photosynthesis taking place.
6. The Pettenkofer tubes; these are long horizontal tubes containing 25 ml. N/10-barium hydroxide (baryta) together with 25 ml. boiled distilled water. A two-way tap is fitted to facilitate easy changing of tubes.
7. Finally, check flasks containing calcium hydroxide to make sure that all the respiratory carbon dioxide has been removed in the Pettenkofer tube.

In setting up the apparatus it is important to use good-quality tubes and rubber bungs, otherwise leaks may result.

PROCEDURE. Weigh out the respiring material and place it in the respiration chamber, test the apparatus for leaks and regulate the flow so as to allow about 100 bubbles per minute through the Pettenkofer tube (filled with 50 ml. distilled water). Meanwhile fill the other Pettenkofer tube with 25 ml. fresh N/10-baryta and 25 ml. boiled distilled water. Cork-up, change the two-way tap, adjust the rate of bubbling and leave for between one and four hours. At the end of this time remove the Pettenkofer tube and pour its contents carefully into a conical flask. Wash the tube with boiled distilled water and add the washings to the flask.

TITRATION. The baryta from the Pettenkofer tube should be titrated immediately against N/10-HCl using phenol phthalein as indicator. During the experiment the carbon dioxide has reacted with the baryta to form insoluble barium carbonate. In the titration the HCl reacts with the unchanged baryta only.

Amount N/10-HCl required $= x$ ml.
Time in hours $= y$ hours

$\therefore$ Amount N/10 baryta that reacted with
the CO_2 in one hour $= \dfrac{25 - x}{y}$ ml.

Thus the amount CO_2 absorbed in
one hour $= \dfrac{(25 - x)}{y} \times \dfrac{11\cdot2}{10}$ ml. at N.T.P.

Knowing the weight of the respiring material, the carbon dioxide production per hour per gm. can be calculated.

During the running of the experiment the normality of the baryta should be checked by titration with N/10-HCl and if necessary, allowance made in the calculation of the results. Accuracy depends to a large extent on efficient handling of the baryta which must be kept in a flask stoppered with a soda-lime tower, the baryta being removed from a tap at the bottom of the flask.

2. Determination of the respiratory quotient (RQ) by means of the Ganong respirometer (see p. 67)

Material. Germinating peas.

Method. Set up two sets of apparatus as shown in fig. 4.5. Fill one apparatus with a strong solution of potassium hydroxide, enclose about 5 gm. of peas in the inverted U-tube, cork-up (if necessary, wax the cork), adjust the level and record that in the graduated tube. As there will be a rise of liquid in this tube, make sure that this starting level is near the bottom of the graduated tube.

Set up a similar apparatus with the same weight of germinating peas but having water or paraffin in the system, in this case arrange for the level of liquid to be half-way up the graduated tube. Record the level and leave both sets of apparatus for twenty-four hours. If really accurate results are to be obtained, a third, control respirometer should also be set up. This should contain water and dead, sterile peas. If it shows any change, adjustments must be made to the readings of the other respirometers.

The amount of oxygen consumed is given by the rise of liquid in the apparatus containing the potassium hydroxide (which absorbs carbon dioxide as soon as it is produced). The amount of carbon dioxide produced is found by comparing the volume changes in both sets of apparatus. If more carbon dioxide is produced than oxygen utilized, then there will be an expansion in the apparatus containing water, and this expansion must be added to the oxygen value to give the amount of carbon dioxide produced. If there is no change in level, then the amount of oxygen utilized is the same as the amount of carbon dioxide released (and the RQ $= 1$). If there is a reduction in volume, then less carbon dioxide is produced than oxygen utilized, and the amount of carbon dioxide produced is given by the oxygen value less this reduction in volume. From these values the RQ of the germinating peas can be calculated:

$$RQ = \frac{\text{Volume carbon dioxide produced}}{\text{Volume oxygen utilized}}$$

3. The Warburg manometric technique (see p. 65)

Principle

In this technique the respiring material is enclosed in the main chamber of a small flask (see figs. 4.3 and 4.4) and kept at a constant temperature in a thermostatically controlled water-bath usually at 25° or 30° C. A small manometer, filled with Brodie's fluid * is attached to the flask and registers any changes in volume due to gases being taken up or produced. In practice, the volume is kept constant by adjustment to the reservoir at the base of the manometer and readings are taken as heights of liquid in the open side of the manometer tube that are required to keep the volume of the flask system unchanged. In many investigations of the respiratory rate the amount of oxygen utilized is found by placing a few drops of strong potassium hydroxide in the centre well, to absorb carbon dioxode. The amount of oxygen taken up in a particular time is given in terms of height changes in the open manometer arm. If these values are to be corrected to cu. mm., then the flask constants must be applied (see exp. 6, below).

The manometer flask is also provided with a side arm from which inhibitors or special substrates can be added once the normal rate of respiration of the material has been determined. The manometer flask is normally arranged to contain 3 ml. It is necessary to sct up a blank, control manometer, the thermobarometer, which should contain 3 ml. of distilled water. This thermobarometer registers any temperature or barometric fluctuation and the readings of the other manometers must bc adjusted to allow for such changes.

Running technique

When the flasks have been filled, carefully grease their stoppers and spigots with vaseline. Take care not to apply too much; it is best to put on a narrow band over the middle of the stopper, a few twists will spread the vaseline and show whether there is a proper seal. The spigot will require two bands of vaseline, make sure that it is closed and properly sealed. The flasks and spigots are kept firmly in position with rubber bands. Open the main valve at the top of the manometer before placing the flasks in the constant temperature tank (see fig. 4.4).

Before the experiment is started the flasks must be allowed to equilibrate for fifteen minutes in the tank to allow their contents to reach the correct temperature. During this time they should be gently shaken at 120 shakes to the minute. At the end of this time adjust the height of the manometers as required, using the reservoir at the bottom of the manometer (both columns should be high at the start for most respiratory experiments), close the main valve of the manometer, read and record the height of both sides of the manometer. Restart the shaking motor and continue taking readings every fifteen minutes. For all subsequent readings the right-hand column is always adjusted to the same height and only the level in the open, left-hand column need be recorded. The respiratory rate should be steady and clearly established after three or four readings, and then the contents of the side arm, if in use, can be added. Unclamp the whole manometer system, put a finger over the open end of the manometer and carefully tip the flask so that the contents of the side arm flow into the main chamber. Replace the manometer and continue readings as before.

It is possible to continue readings for about two hours before lack of oxygen in the flask begins to affect the results. At the end of the experiment open the top valve to prevent the contents of the manometer sucking back into the flask. Wipe off the vaseline from the spigot and joints using cotton-wool and a little xylol, rinse out in soapy water and leave the flasks and spigots soaking overnight in chromic acid. It is most important to have the flasks properly clean before the start of the next experiment.

A note on the apparatus. Although a complete apparatus, consisting of a thermostatically controlled water-bath together with two sets of seven manometers, can be obtained from biological suppliers, it is an expensive item, and it is possible (see fig. 4.4) to construct a useful manometer mostly out of old laboratory equipment. All that is necessary is an electric heating element such as would be used in a kettle, an accurate thermostat, a stirring and shaking motor. Three is the minimum number of manometer units, and these can be purchased for about £10. The shaking and stirring equipment will require some ingenuity in their construction, but the time spent should be well worthwhile.

4. Determination of the respiratory quotient by Warburg manometry (see p. 65)

Material. Two lots of 50, 1-cm. long root tips of barley. These are obtained by sowing the seed thinly on wide-mesh gauze, which is held above damp blotting paper in a covered dish. Wash them well with distilled water before use and count them out on to moist filter-paper.

Method. As described in exp. 3 (p. 179). The constant-temperature bath should be adjusted to 30° C., and three flasks are filled as follows:

Flask	Purpose	Main chamber	Centre well	Side arm	Total
1	Thermo-barometer	3 ml. water	Nil	Nil	3 ml.
2	O_2 uptake	50 root tips; 2·5 ml. distilled water	0·5 ml. strong KOH; filter-paper wick	Nil	3 ml.
3	$\dfrac{CO_2}{O_2}$	50 root tips; 2·5 ml. distilled water	0·5 ml. distilled water	Nil	3 ml.

Do not use a mouth pipette for the potassium hydroxide.

The apparatus should be allowed to run for at least an hour. Then corrections for the thermobarometer and the flask constants should be applied and the total oxygen uptake compared with the total carbon dioxide production as in exp. 2 above.

5. Investigation of the effect of addition of the inhibitor KCN on the rate of respiration (see p. 75)

Material. As described in exp. 4 above.

Method. As described in exp. 3 above. The constant-temperature tank should be adjusted to 30° C., and the three flasks are filled as follows:

Flask	Purpose	Main chamber	Centre well	Side arm	Total
1	Thermo-barometer	3 ml. water	Nil	Nil	3 ml.
2	O_2 uptake with $M/1,000$-KCN	50 root tips; 2·0 ml. phosphate buffer pH 6·5	0·5 ml. strong KOH; filter-paper wick	0·5 ml. $M/200$-KCN	3 ml.
3	O_2 uptake with $M/10,000$-KCN	50 root tips; 2·0 ml. phosphate buffer pH 6·5	0·5 ml. strong KOH; filter-paper wick	0·5 ml. $M/2,000$-KCN	3 ml.

Do not use a mouth pipette for the potassium hydroxide or cyanide.

For details of the making up of the phosphate buffer see p. 205. After about an hour, when the respiration rates of the root tips are steady, tip the cyanide from the side arms. Continue readings for another hour, then, after applying thermobarometer and flask constant corrections, compare the percentage inhibition.

6. Calculation of the flask constants for the Warburg manometer

It is necessary that the flask constants (K) of each flask (together with their own manometer tubes) be calculated if the changes in height of the manometer arm are to be converted from mm. to cu. mm. of gas at N.T.P. Once determined for any particular temperature, they must be carefully recorded and kept for future reference, as they are needed in calculating the results in all manometric experiments.

K can be calculated from the following equation:

$$K = \frac{V_g \frac{273}{T} + V_f \alpha}{P_0}$$

where V_g = volume gas alone in cu. mm. (not the liquid);
     T = absolute temperature;
     V_f = volume of liquid in the flask in cu. mm.;
     α = solubility of the gas (ml. at N.T.P. dissolved by 1 ml. water at 1 atm.);
Take V_f = 3,000;
     α O_2 at 25° C. = 0·028;
          at 30° C. = 0·027;
       CO_2 at 25° C. = 0·077;
          at 30° C. = 0·067;
     P_0 = 10,000;
     V_g, the gas volume of the flask + the manometer bore to the zero mark has to be determined, as follows:

Make sure that the flask is dry and clean and weigh it with its spigot to three places. Then fill it with distilled water and insert the spigot. The flask should be filled up to its neck, so that when it is attached to the manometer the liquid rises up into the manometer tube; mark the point to which it rises. Withdraw the flask carefully and reweigh. Calculate the volume of the flask by subtracting the dry weight of the flask from this value. Measure the remaining length of manometer tube to the zero mark and calculate its volume, assuming the bore to have a diameter of 1 mm. Add this volume to that of the flask to obtain V_g.

7. Identification of acetaldehyde as an intermediate in anaerobic respiration (see p. 71)

Material. Freshly washed yeast that has been growing actively. This can be obtained by keeping a culture of baker's yeast in well-aerated water and supplied with glucose and nutrients. Centrifuge this yeast suspension. Reject the supernatant. Resuspend the yeast in distilled water and centrifuge again. Once more

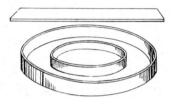

FIG. A.12. The Conway unit.

reject the supernatant. This process can be repeated until all the nutrients and waste products have been removed.

Method. Place 1 ml. freshly washed yeast paste in the outer part of a Conway unit (see fig. A.12) add 1 ml. distilled water and mix. Place 1 ml. 0·1 per cent 2:4-dinitrophenylhydrazine in the centre well of the unit. Add 1 ml. 1 per cent glucose or 1 ml. 1 per cent pyruvic acid to the outer part and seal the unit immediately, using a little vaseline to ensure an air-tight seal. Rock gently to mix the materials in the outer part only and incubate at under 10° C. for about ten hours. Examine for brown crystals of the hydrazone, which are formed if acetaldehyde has been formed by the yeast and has diffused over from the outer part of the unit. If the incubation is carried out at temperatures much higher than 10° C. the pyruvic acid may vaporize and react with the dinitrophenylhydrazine. Careful controls should be set up to check that this does not happen.

8. Identification of some plant acids by simple chemical tests (see p. 71)

Materials. *Bryophyllum* or *Sedum* spp.

Method. Squash a few leaves in a mortar, filter or centrifuge to clear the extract of chloroplasts and cell-wall detritus. Neutralize the extract carefully with dilute sodium hydroxide and divide into two parts. Test these with the various reagents as indicated in the table below:

PART 1			PART 2		
First add a few drops 5% CaCl₂	*Then add an equal quantity of glacial acetic acid and boil*	*Then cool and add 95% alcohol*	*First add a few drops 5% lead acetate*	*Then add an equal quantity of glacial acetic acid and warm*	PLANT ACID
White ppt.	White ppt.	White ppt.	White ppt.	White ppt.	OXALIC
Nil	Nil	Nil	White ppt.	Ppt. dissolves in cold	MALIC
Nil	Nil	Nil	White ppt.	Ppt. dissolves on warming	CITRIC
Nil	Nil	White ppt.	White ppt.	White ppt. dissolves slightly	TARTARIC

9. Identification of plant acids by chromatography (see p. 71).

Material. Leaves of *Bryophyllum* or *Sedum* spp.

Method. Full details are given on p. 164. Squash a few leaves in a mortar, if necessary adding a little 70 per cent ethanol or distilled water. Load plenty of extract on to the chromatogram. The most satisfactory technique is that using *n*-butyl formate solvent.

10. Investigation of polyphenol oxidase as an example of a terminal oxidase (see pp. 76 and 118)

Material. Fresh potato. Some strains work better than others and younger tubers give better results.

Method.

Preparation of an extract of the enzyme

Cut up half a potato into small chunks, grind in a mortar with 10 ml. distilled water and filter the extract through glass wool at a Büchner funnel. Centrifuge to precipitate the starch grains and cell wall detritus.

Test for polyphenol oxidase activity

The enzyme will cause the conversion of guaiacum (freshly made by dissolving a little guaiacum resin in absolute alcohol to give a pale-brown solution) into guaiacum blue. Add 0·5 ml. guaiacum to 3 ml. of the enzyme extract and note the blue colour produced.

Characterization of polyphenol oxidase

(a) EFFECT OF TEMPERATURE ON THE ACTIVITY OF THE ENZYME. Prepare water-baths at 40° and 70° C., place test-tubes containing 3 ml. enzyme extract in the water-baths and then add 0·5 ml. guaiacum extract. Note the time taken for the blue colour to appear and compare with the time taken at room temperature. How does temperature affect the activity of the enzyme?

(b) EFFECT OF pH ON THE ACTIVITY OF THE ENZYME. Prepare phosphate buffer solutions (see p. 205) of pH 3·0, 5·5, 7·0, 8·0. Place 2 ml. of each buffer in separate test-tubes and add 1 ml. enzyme extract and 0·5 ml. guaiacum to each. Note the colours produced over a period of time. At what pH does the enzyme operate most efficiently?

(c) EFFECT OF CYANIDE INHIBITOR ON THE ACTIVITY OF THE ENZYME. Prepare two test-tubes with 3 ml. enzyme extract in each. To one add 0·5 ml. M/500-KCN and then add 0·5 ml. guaiacum to both. As polyphenol oxidase contains a copper activator group, inhibition or a slowing up of the reaction should result as cyanide forms complexes with metals such as copper and iron. Add 6 drops 1 per cent $CuSO_4$ to both tubes; is inhibition reversed? Make up a test-tube with enzyme, cyanide and $CuSO_4$ but no guaiacum to check that the resulting colour obtained after reversal of the inhibition is not wholly due to a $CuSO_4$–KCN complex being formed.

11. Investigation of the dehydrogenase activity of etiolated pea shoots
(see pp. 76 and 118)

Material. A washed suspension of yeast (see p. 182); pea seedlings grown in the dark for some days.

Method.

Preparation of an extract of the enzyme from pea seedlings

Squash up a few etiolated shoots in a mortar with 10 ml. ice-cold phosphate buffer pH 6·5 (see p. 205). Centrifuge at medium speed for five minutes to clear the extract and treat the supernatant as follows; the washed yeast suspension may be used direct:

(a) TEST FOR DEHYDROGENASE ACTIVITY. Dehydrogenase enzymes cause bleaching of redox dyes such as dilute alkaline methylene blue or better, very dilute 2:6-dichlorophenolindophenol (DCPIP)† at the more satisfactory pH 6·5. Such bleaching occurs more quickly if no oxygen is present; accordingly, it is best to operate the following tests in small-sized test-tubes, which give less surface area for oxidation, or else in special Thunberg tubes (see fig. A.13). The air can be removed from such tubes using a vacuum pump.

Take 1 ml. of the enzyme extract or suspension and place this in the main part of the Thunberg tube and add 0·5 ml. DCPIP to the side arm. Adjust the side arm so that the tube can be evacuated and connect it up to a vacuum pump. After a few minutes close the tap by rotating the side arm and disconnect the vacuum pump. Tip the DCPIP dye from the side arm into the main part of the tube and take the time for the dye to become reduced and bleached.

† Note: this is also a test for ascorbic acid (vitamin C), which may interfere with the reaction.

(b) EFFECT OF TEMPERATURE ON THE ACTIVITY OF THE ENZYME. Repeat the experiment described in the above section at a series of temperatures, e.g. 30°, 40°, 50°, 60° C., using a water-bath to obtain the desired temperature and allowing the solutions in the Thunberg tube a few minutes to reach the correct temperature before tipping the side arm. Record the time taken for the bleaching to occur in each case. Plot $1/\text{time}$ against temperature on a graph.

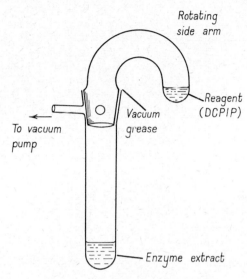

FIG. A.13. The Thunberg tube.
A device for estimating the activity of dehydrogenase enzymes.

12. Spectroscopic examination of the cytochromes (see p. 77)

Material. Actively growing baker's yeast.

Method. Centrifuge some freshly grown yeast and resuspend the precipitated paste in cool, freshly boiled water. Add a little 10 per cent dithionite (sodium hydrosulphite, a mild reducing agent) to help intensify the bands and recentrifuge. Spread the paste on a slide so as to form a layer at least 2 mm. thick, cover with another side and illuminate with a high-intensity microscope lamp. View through a low-dispersion hand spectrometer and note the incidence of absorption bands. These may be visible as follows:

Part of the spectrum	Wavelength in mμ	Strength	Type of cytochrome	Absorption band
Red	603	Weak band	Cytochrome *a*	α
Yellow	563	Strong band	Cytochrome *b*	α
Yellow–green	550	Very strong band	Cytochrome *c*	α
Green–blue	c.525	Weak band	Cytochrome *a, b, c*	β

APPENDIX TO CHAPTER 5

1. The use of water cultures for investigating the plant's requirement for various minerals
2. The culture of fungi on agar media for investigating their mineral requirement
3. Investigation of the effect of boron and glucose on the germination of pollen grains
4. Determination of the effect of anaerobic conditions and low temperatures on the absorption of bromide ions by excised barley roots
5. Determination of the effect of anaerobic conditions and low temperature on the absorption of ammonium ions by carrot discs, using the Conway method for estimating ammonia
6. Investigation of the salt respiration effect using the Warburg manometer
7. Estimation of the fixed nitrogen in plant material by the micro-Kjeldahl technique
8. Investigation of the rate of uptake of dissolved mineral by the use of P^{32} radioactive tracer
9. Investigation of the path of movement of dissolved mineral in the stem by the use of P^{32} radioactive tracer
10. Investigation of the areas of accumulation of phosphate by autoradiographic analysis of P^{32}

1. The use of water cultures for investigating the plant's requirement for various minerals (see p. 85)

Material. Barley seed.
Method.
(i) *Preparation of young seedlings*
Take an old cork mat and drill a series of small holes of about $\frac{1}{2}$ cm. in diameter through it. Paint wax over the whole mat and float it in a trough of water. Place a seed over each hole and leave them to germinate. After about ten days the leaves should be quite well developed; transfer the seedlings to the culture solution bottles.
(ii) *Preparation of the culture bottles*
Half-pint milk bottles make useful containers. Wash seven of them well with boiling water, followed by distilled water, and then fit them with carefully cleaned corks which have been drilled with $\frac{1}{2}$-in.-diameter holes. If an air pump is available it is a great advantage to provide the bottles with aeration tubes, as growth rates are more than doubled if the roots are kept well aerated.
(iii) *Preparation of the culture solutions*
The complete medium is made up as follows:

(From James: *An Introduction to Plant Physiology*, by permission of the Clarendon Press, Oxford.)

$CaSO_4.2H_2O$	0·25 gm.
$Ca(H_2PO_4)_2.H_2O$	0·25 gm.
$MgSO_4.7H_2O$	0·25 gm.
NaCl	0·08 gm.
KNO_3	0·70 gm.
$FeCl_3.6H_2O$	0·005 gm.

Make up to 1 litre.

For cultures lacking various elements substitute as follows:

Potassium:	replace	KNO_3	by	0·59 gm. $NaNO_3$
Calcium:	replace	$\begin{cases} CaSO_4.2H_2O \\ Ca(H_2PO_4)_2.H_2O \end{cases}$	by by	0·20 gm. K_2SO_4 0·71 gm. $Na_2HPO_4.12H_2O$
Iron:	omit	$FeCl_3.6H_2O$		
Nitrogen:	replace	KNO_3	by	0·52 gm. KCl
Phosphorus:	replace	$Ca(H_2PO_4)_2.H_2O$	by	0·16 gm. $Ca(NO_3)_2$
Sulphur:	replace	$\begin{cases} CaSO_4.2H_2O \\ MgSO_4.7H_2O \end{cases}$	by by	0·16 gm. $CaCl_2$ 0·21 gm. $MgCl_2$

Fill the bottles with the required nutrient, cover them with black paper to reduce algal growth and label them. Place a barley seedling in each so that the seed is just below the top of the cork and keep it in place with a pad of dry cotton-wool. Place the bottles in a well-lit place, turn on the aerating system, if it is available, and leave for some weeks. The cotton-wool will probably become damp, so it should be renewed as often as possible to reduce the risk of fungal infection. The culture solutions should be renewed every fortnight, and loss due to evaporation and transpiration should be made good by topping-up with distilled water.

2. The culture of fungi on agar media for investigating their mineral requirement (see p. 87)

Material. Mucor or any actively growing species.

Method.

Preparation of general nutrient agar

It is first necessary to grow the fungus so as to obtain it in an actively growing, uniform and pure state. A most useful medium for this purpose is known as potato agar and is made up as follows:

Take 200 gm. of clean peeled potatoes and chop them up as finely as possible into 200 ml. of water. Boil for about half an hour and then allow to settle and cool. Filter through muslin and make the solution up to 400 ml. in a large flask, add 10 gm. of agar and place in an autoclave at 30 lb per sq. in. for ten minutes. The medium is then sterile and ready for pouring on to Petri dishes that have been sterilized previously. Once the plates have cooled and the agar set, they can be inoculated by means of a sterile needle touched on to the surface of the stock fungus culture. When fungi are first isolated from wild cultures they grow much better on the above medium, but for the investigation of their mineral requirements it is necessary to make up a special medium:

N

Preparation of special media for investigating the requirement of the fungus for various minerals

Add 10 gm. of agar and 20 gm. of glucose to 400 ml. of distilled water and heat until they are dissolved. The following nutrients are required for a complete medium of 400 ml. Different nutrient media can be made up by omitting any one mineral and substituting another as in exp. 1 above.

$(NH_4)_2HPO_4$	0·5 gm.
KNO_3	0·4 gm.
$CaCl_2$	0·2 gm.
$MgSO_4.7H_2O$	0·2 gm.
$FeCl_3.6H_2O$	0·002 gm.
Biotin (vitamin B1 or thiamin)	0·5 gm.

Add the desired minerals and sterilize the media as above. Pour the sterile agar on to sterile Petri dishes and inoculate with fresh and actively growing fungus. Growth should start in about two days, and measurements of the size of the cultures can be made over a period of time; for this, measurement of the diameter of the colony is sufficient, in most cases.

Note. For full details of a wide variety of media used for culturing micro-organisms, see *The Oxoid Manual of Culture Media*, 2nd edn. (1962), issued by the Oxoid Division, Oxo Ltd., Southwark Bridge Road, London S.E.1.

3. Investigation of the effect of boron and glucose on the germination of pollen grains (see p. 87)

Material. Various pollen, e.g. tulip (*Tulipa*), bluebell (*Endymion*), honey-suckle (*Lonicera*), plantain (*Plantago*) or columbine (*Aquilegia*).

Method. Make up nine mixtures of glucose and sodium borate in water, so that the following concentrations are obtained; there should be about 5 ml. of each solution.

No.	Per cent glucose	Per cent borate
1	0	0·0
2	0	0·0001
3	0	0·01
4	10	0·0
5	10	0·0001
6	10	0·01
7	20	0·0
8	20	0·0001
9	20	0·01

It is probably simplest to make these up from stock solutions of borate (0·01 per cent), adding the correct quantity of glucose as required. Ideally, these solutions should be sterilized. Prepare nine Petri dishes, insert a filter-paper in each and then add about 3 ml. of one of the above solutions so as to moisten the filter-paper thoroughly.

Cut squares, circles and triangles of cellophane each about 2 cm. across. Dust one surface of a piece of cellophane with pollen and place it on the moistened filter-paper. Make a note of the shape of cellophane indicating a type of pollen. In this way several sorts of pollen grain may be investigated at the same time. Cover the Petri dishes and leave them in a warm place for about 24 hours. At the end of this time remove each piece of cellophane with a pair of tweezers, place it on a slide and examine in water under a coverslip, using low and high power. Compare the number of pollen tubes formed in the various nutrients and make what deductions you can regarding the nutritional requirements of pollen for germination.

4. Determination of the effect of anaerobic conditions and low temperatures on the absorption of bromide ions by excised barley roots (see p. 93)

Material. Actively growing barley seedlings (see exp. 4 on p. 180).
Alternatively, washed carrot discs may be used (see exp. 5 below).
Method. Cut off 300 tips of barley root 1 cm. long into a beaker of distilled water. Wash well in distilled water at a Büchner funnel and count on to moist filter-paper so that they can be transferred to the solutions. One hundred ml. of M/200-potassium bromide are pipetted into each of three large conical flasks. Flasks one and two are aerated by a motor, and flask two is placed in a trough packed with ice and maintained at about 3° C. Flask three is bubbled through with nitrogen from a cylinder; the solution in this flask should previously be boiled under reduced pressure to remove dissolved oxygen. It must be brought back to atmospheric pressure by allowing nitrogen to bubble into the solution. One hundred root tips are then placed in each flask.

While the experiment is running the strength of the M/200-KBr can be checked and the titration technique perfected. Pipette 25 ml. of the KBr into a stoppered flask, add 2·5 ml. N-acetic acid so that the acid is N/10 before titration and finally add 6 drops of 2 per cent aqueous eosin as an indicator. Titrate against M/50-AgNO₃, shaking the solution vigorously to facilitate the absorption of the eosin upon the precipitated AgBr. The end point is reached when the AgBr precipitate turns magenta. Calculate the gm. per litre of bromide in the stock solution. After about three hours take the temperature of the experimental flasks, decant off the liquid and adjust the volume of each flask to allow for any evaporation that may have taken place, and determine how much bromide has been absorbed by the root segments in each case. Lay out your results in table form, expressing the uptake of bromide under nitrogen and low-temperature conditions as a percentage of the absorption in air at room temperature. (After Brierley (1958). *School Science Review*, No. 138, p. 254.)

5. Determination of the effect of anaerobic conditions and low temperature on the absorption of ammonium ions by carrot discs, using the Conway method for estimating ammonia (see p. 93)

Material. Thirty uniform carrot discs, washed in running water for about twelve hours.

Method. Set up three flasks as in exp. 4, but fill each with 100 ml. N/50-ammonium phosphate $(NH_4)_2HPO_4$. Place ten weighed discs in each flask, cork up and adjust the bubbling gas. After about six hours the discs may be filtered off and the concentration of ammonium estimated. Meanwhile the N/50-ammonium phosphate should be checked and the estimation technique perfected.

The Conway method for estimating ammonia

Pipette 2 ml. of the ammonium solution into the outer chamber of the Conway unit (see fig. A.12). Pipette 1·5 ml. borate buffer (see pp. 91 and 204) into the centre well, grease the rim of the unit and add 1 ml. strong sodium hydroxide to the outer chamber using a pipette fitted with a rubber bulb. Seal the unit rock it gently (do not mix the inner and outer liquids) and incubate at 40° C. for about two hours. Then remove the cover and add N/50-HCl from a burette to the centre well until it regains its original colour (i.e. it turns back, from blue to pink). Calculate the efficiency of 'recovery' of ammonia and make the necessary allowance when titrating the unknown samples. Record your results in table form, expressing the uptake of ammonium under nitrogen and low-temperature conditions as a percentage of the absorption in air at room temperature. Allow for any small weight differences in the carrot discs.

6. Investigation of the salt respiration effect using the Warburg manometer (see p. 93)

Material. A culture of the yeast-like fungus, *Torilopsis utilis*, or similar species, which has been growing on nitrogen-deficient medium.

Method. As described in exp. 4 (p. 180) above. The constant-temperature tank should be adjusted to 25° C. and the three flasks are filled as follows:

Flask	Purpose	Main chamber	Centre well	Side arm	Total
1	Thermo-barometer	3 ml. water	Nil	Nil	3 ml.
2	O_2 uptake: NH_3 sampled at end	2·2 ml. yeast suspension	0·3 ml. strong KOH; filter-paper wick	0·5 ml. $M/30$-$(NH_4)_2HPO_4$	3 ml.
3	O_2 uptake; NH_3 sampled at end	2.2 ml. yeast suspension	0·3 ml. strong KOH; filter-paper wick	0·5 ml. $M/30$-Na_2HPO_4	3 ml.

Do not use a mouth pipette for the potassium hydroxide.

After about an hour, when the respiration rates of the yeast are steady, tip on the phosphate from the side arms. Continue readings for another hour, then dismantle the flasks. After applying thermobarometer and flask constant corrections, compare the percentage stimulation on addition of sodium and ammonium phosphate.

The ammonium content of the yeast and the external solution are then determined for each flask. In flask 2 (which should have shown a rise in the respiration rate on the addition of ammonium phosphate) the fungus should have taken up a considerable quantity of ammonia, thus leaving the external solution less concentrated. Flask 3, which should not have shown much respiratory response on the addition of the sodium phosphate, acts as a control, and the quantity of ammonia normally present in the yeast can be determined so that the actual take-up in flask 2 can be found. The ammonia can be determined either by the micro-Kjeldahl technique (see exp. 7 below) or by the Conway method (see exp. 5 above).

7. Estimation of the fixed nitrogen in plant material by the micro-Kjeldahl technique (see p. 101)

Material. Two sets of pea seedlings that have been grown on sterile and unsterile soil; the latter should have developed root nodules and would be expected to have a higher level of fixed nitrogen than the former.

Method.

Digestion of the material to convert the various nitrogenous compounds to ammonia

Place a weighed quantity (about 10 gm.) of material of one set in a 100-ml. conical flask (treat material of the other set in a similar manner throughout the course of the experiment) and add 1 ml. of 50 per cent sulphuric acid. Place a watch-glass over the mouth of the flask and heat gently in a fume cupboard for several hours (usually overnight). The material will dissolve, leaving a sticky black solution. Then cool the flask and add two drops of saturated potassium persulphate solution and heat the flask again, with the watch-glass over its mouth, until the solution becomes colourless (this will probably take at least an hour). This operation should be carried out in a fume cupboard.

Distillation of the ammonia

When the solution is clear, cool the flask and pour its contents carefully into the distillation flask E (see fig. A.14), through the funnel G. Wash the flask twice with a little distilled water and add the washings to the distillation flask. Then add 5 ml. distilled water containing 5 drops of bromothymol blue indicator, followed by sodium hydroxide, until the solution goes bright blue.

Prepare 100 ml. 2 per cent solution of boric acid (or alternatively use a borate buffer *). Place 5 ml. of this acid in the flask I and add three drops of thymol blue indicator; top up with distilled water until the end of the condenser dips below the surface of the liquid.

Open the tap B, close tap D and boil the water in the flask A. Adjust the rate of boiling so that steam is bubbling steadily and rapidly through the distillation flask E without letting liquid splash up the neck of the flask. The ammonia is carried by the steam into the condenser H and collects in the flask I. In a short while the indicator in I will turn blue, indicating that the ammonia is distilling over, the flask can be removed after a further two minutes.

Titration technique

The ammonia that has distilled over reacts with the boric acid:

$$NH_3 + H_3BO_3 \longrightarrow NH_4^+ + H_2BO_3^-$$

The pH becomes higher and the thymol blue changes colour. When the distillation is complete the borate solution is titrated back to its original colour (compare with a standard) using $N/70$-H_2SO_4. At this point all the NH_4 has combined with the H_2SO_4, since this acid is stronger than the H_3BO_3.

$$2NH_4^+ + 2H_2BO_3^- + H_2SO_4 \longrightarrow 2NH_4^+ + SO_4^= + 2H_3BO_3$$

Knowing that 1 ml. $N/70$-H_2SO_4 represents 0·2 mg. nitrogen per litre, the amount of nitrogen in the original sample can be calculated. However, it is also necessary to run a 'water-blank' using distilled water, and it is also wise to check the efficiency of the apparatus by using a known ammonium sulphate solution (which needs no preliminary digestion).

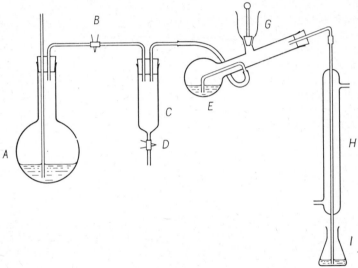

Fig. A.14. The micro-Kjeldahl apparatus.

Washing of the apparatus

After distillation is complete, remove the flame and close the valve B. Steam will condense in C, and the contents of E will suck back into C. Empty C by opening D. Wash G and E with 10 ml. of distilled water (if necessary made slightly acid with dilute H_2SO_4) and arrange for this to be sucked back into C. The apparatus is again ready for use.

8. Investigation of the rate of uptake of dissolved mineral by the use of P^{32} radioactive tracer (see p. 96)

Material. Two young rooted plants of tomato, *Zebrina* (*Tradescantia*), balsam (*Impatiens sultani*), or of a woody perennial, such as willow or *Skimmia*. If possible these cuttings should be rooted in water or nutrient solution, as it is difficult to avoid damage if they are dug up from soil. If they have been grown in soil, transference to nutrient medium a few weeks before the experiment will be satisfactory. Aeration considerably helps growth under these conditions.

Method. First cover the bench top with thick, waterproof paper. All apparatus should stand on enamel trays. Make up the test solution by preparing 100 ml. M/15-phosphate buffer (see p. 205) and add sufficient radioactive phosphate to give the solution a strength of between 3 and 6 micro-curies (μc). Take care when pipetting out the solution of P^{32}; use rubber gloves and a special pipette with a bulb or piston system for sucking up the liquid, *under no circumstances use an ordinary mouth pipette.* Cut a thin piece of lead to cover the culture jar (see fig. 5.12), leaving a slit for the plant stem. Wedge the plant in carefully with a small piece of cotton-wool and fill the jar with the tracer solution. Prepare a similar control specimen, but omit the P^{32}; leave both plants in a well-illuminated and aerated place. If the plants' roots are small, the tracer may be placed in a small tube, such as a specimen tube, inside the larger jar. The specimen tube may be kept in place by means of Plasticine.

Using a ratemeter, estimate the counts per minute at a given position, say 1 in. from the main apex; the control is useful for comparing the background counts of the two specimens at the start. Record at frequent intervals until the counts per minute reach several hundred. This will take about one day for the annuals, usually longer for woody plants. Plot the counts per minute against time on a graph, and thus obtain an idea of the rate of absorption of the phosphate. The experiment could be repeated under different external conditions to find the effect of environmental factors on the rate of uptake.

For full details of regulations and precautions see p. 172. P^{32}, although a fairly strong β-emitter (1·71 MeV), has most of its radiation absorbed by glassware. Its short half-life (14·2 days) makes waste disposal simple as solutions may be stored until their activity is negligible.

9. Investigation of the path of movement of dissolved mineral in the stem by the use of P^{32} radioactive tracer (see p. 97)

Material. Two rooted cuttings of a woody plant prepared as in the above experiment.

Method. Make up the nutrient solution as described above, but so as to produce 200 ml. solution with a count of 6 microcuries. Place 100 ml. of the tracer solution in each of two small jars and insert a rooted plant in one jar and a similar but ringed plant in the other, enclosing each with lead as in exp. 8. When ringing the stem take a scalpel and cut through the bark and phloem so as to make two rings 1 cm. apart. Remove the bark in between and scrape off any phloem and cambium (the slimy tissues) remaining. Estimate the counts per minute as in exp. 8. Has ringing made any difference to the accumulation of phosphate in the upper parts of the plant? Record the uptake against time on a graph for the two plants.

10. Investigation of the areas of accumulation of phosphate by autoradiographic analysis of P^{32} (see p. 97)

Materials. As produced in exp. 8 and 9 above.

Method. Remove the specimen from the culture jar, rinse off the nutrient solution thoroughly and dry it with tissue (use rubber gloves and dispose of the tissues in the bin allocated for radioactive waste). Alternatively, cut off the aerial parts and analyse these alone. Make an autoradiograph of the specimens as described on p. 174. Exposure time will be about 36 hours, with Kodirex and material giving a count of about 1,000 per minute 1 in. from the material. What conclusions can you draw about the distribution of P^{32} in the stem, apex and leaves of the specimen?

APPENDIX TO CHAPTER 6

1. Squash preparations of chromosomes
2. Simple tests for proteins
3. Chromatographic identification of amino-acids and proteins
4. Quantitative estimation of glucose and reducing sugars
5. Identification of simple sugars by chromatography
6. Polarimetric study of the inversion of sucrose
7. Extraction, purification and properties of starch phosphorylase
8. Identification of structural carbohydrates
9. Identification of anthocyanin and anthoxanthin pigments
10. Identification of lipids

1. Squash preparations of chromosomes (see p. 106)

Materials. Onion (*Allium cepa*) is very useful for root-tip preparations. Anthers of *Tradescantia*, *Fritillaria*, *Allium* and *Paeonia* spp. are suitable for meiosis. (Mitosis is also frequently observed in the developing anther.)

Method. This method normally uses *no* fixation. Alternatively, 24 hours fixation in Carnoy le Brun (1 part glacial acetic acid, 1 part chloroform, 1 part absolute alcohol) can be used and gives good results, especially with pollen-grain meiosis material.

Cut the anther or root tip from the living plant and warm it in aceto-lacmoid + HCl * stain for five minutes. A watch-glass and spirit lamp are useful for this purpose.

Cut off a small part of the end of the root tip or part of the anther; macerate it with a needle and mount under a round No. 1 cover-slip in aceto-orcein * stain. Tap with the wooden end of the needle, using a blotting-paper pad over the cover-slip to spread the material. Care must be taken not to move the cover-slip. Warm gently two or three times during the tapping to help spread the material and lessen cytoplasmic staining.

When examining the preparation correct lighting is important and green filtering is most beneficial. The best squashes should be examined with an oil-immersion lens.

Permanent preparations

These can be made by first smearing egg albumen over the cover-slip and warming it. The material will then stick to the cover-slip, and this may be removed by floating it off in 45 per cent acetic acid. Dehydrate quickly and mount in Euparal.

Note: If fresh material is used most of the staining is done by the aceto-orcein; if fixed material is used the lacmoid is the main staining agent. In the first case the HCl in the lacmoid is important in aiding the penetration of the stain by macerating the tissues. Lack of fixation sometimes results in rather bubbly chromosomes, which occasionally appear double; care is required in interpreting such preparations.

2. Simple tests for proteins (see p. 117)

Materials. Protoplasm is made-up largely of proteins and amino-acids, so that considerable quantities are found in any living cell or tissue; they are particularly concentrated in rapidly growing meristematic areas, especially the stem and root apices.

Tests.

(i) MILLON'S TEST (Cole's version).* Add a little Millon's 'A' * to the protein, boil, allow to cool; a pale-yellow colour indicates a considerable quantity of protein. Add a drop of Millon's 'B',* a red colour, produced on warming, indicates the presence of the amino-acid *tyrosine*, which is common both as a constituent of proteins and also as a free amino-acid.

(ii) XANTHOPROTEIC TEST. Place about 2 ml. of the protein solution in a test-tube and add a few drops of concentrated nitric acid. A cloudy precipitate is formed which turns yellow on boiling. After cooling add ammonium hydroxide until the solution is alkaline, when it will turn orange. This is a general test for proteins.

(iii) BIURET TEST. Warm the tissue to be tested in a little distilled water. To this add 2 ml. of 40 per cent sodium hydroxide and one drop of 1 per cent copper sulphate. A pale lilac colour, produced on warming, indicates proteins.

(iv) IODINE DISSOLVED IN POTASSIUM IODIDE. This gives a golden-brown colour with proteins, but also with several other substances; it is, however, particularly useful in helping to show up the cytoplasm and nucleus.

3. Chromatographic identification of amino-acids and proteins (see p. 115)

Materials. Young and actively metabolizing tissues such as seedlings and root tips.

Method. Grind up the tissue in a mortar with a little 80 per cent ethanol and spot the extract on to the chromatogram. The chromatogram technique is as described p. 164, the best solvent being phenol.

Amino-acids will appear without special treatment; proteins themselves will not show up on the chromatogram, but their amino-acids can be released by heating the original extract to 100° C. with 6N-hydrochloric acid in a sealed tube for a few minutes.

4. Quantitative estimation of glucose and reducing sugars (see p. 124)

Principle. Alkaline ferricyanide is reduced on heating to the ferro state by the reducing sugar. The amount of ferrocyanide is then estimated by oxidizing it back to the ferri state with dichromate, using diphenylamine as an *internal* indicator. The concentration of dichromate is such that 1 ml. of it is equivalent to 1 mg. of glucose.

Reagents. 13·2 gm. potassium ferricyanide ⎫ to 1 litre H_2O.
          80·0 gm. anhydrous sodium carbonate ⎭

Dissolve the Na_2CO_3 in 850 ml. H_2O with gentle heat, cool and then add the ferricyanide and make up to a litre. Store in a darkened (brown) bottle. The reagent keeps for at least six months. If a slight sediment forms after a few weeks, then filter it off. Exact weights are not necessary for the above mixture: the nearest centigram is sufficiently accurate.

Diphenylamine: 0·2 per cent in *conc.* sulphuric acid. 15 ml. of this solution to be made up to a litre with 5 per cent (by vol.) H_2SO_4. This final solution will also keep at least six months.

Potassium dichromate: 1·60 gm. dissolved in H_2O and made up to a litre keeps indefinitely.

Method. Using a pipette fitted with a rubber bulb, pipette 10 ml. of K-ferricyanide solution into a boiling tube (approx. 18 × 3 cm.) and add (see note (*a*)) 20 ml. of the unknown sugar solution from a pipette. Immerse in a boiling water-bath for fifteen minutes and then cool. This is best done in a running cold water-bath, when it takes about two minutes. For these baths, short square biscuit tins with string stretched across to form roughly 3-cm. squares are quite convenient.

To the cooled digest add 15 ml. (measuring cylinder) of diphenylamine indicator. This must be done fairly slowly, since CO_2 evolution takes place. *At once*, titrate with the standard dichromate until a permanent smoky appearance pervades the whole solution. This is best done by rotating the boiling tube in the right hand while the burette tap is manipulated by the left. White paper behind the boiling tube greatly helps one to see the first appearance of the smokiness. A blank should be run (using 20 ml. distilled water in place of unknown sugar), and the dichromate equivalent (which is usually about 0·2 ml.) subtracted from all subsequent dichromate amounts of unknown sugar solutions.

Then 1 ml. dichromate = 1 mg. of reducing sugar, *as glucose*.

Notes. (*a*) The unknown sugar must be less than 13·5 mg. as glucose per 20 ml. aliquot. If it is more, then the digest, on boiling, will be completely reduced and become virtually colourless, and the unknown sample is then lost. However, the range of the method can be greatly increased simply by using smaller aliquots of the unknown *and making up the difference to 20 ml. with distilled water*. Thus, 2, 5, 10, 15 (10 + 5) aliquots of unknown can be pipetted out and the requisite difference of distilled water added by measuring cylinder. It is most important that the digest to be put in the boiling water-bath is composed of 10 ml. ferricyanide + 20 ml. of unknown (total = 30 ml.), but it does not matter if the 20 ml. of unknown is made up of 2 ml., 5 ml., etc., of actual sugar extract, provided the difference from 20 ml. is made up with distilled water. *In short, sugar sample plus distilled water must always equal 20 ml.* The reason for this is that the reduction by sugar is never stoichiometric and depends on alkalinity and time of heating. If, therefore, the digest is of varying volume, then the pH will also vary and erratic results will ensue. But the distilled water difference does not have to be accurately measured out, and a measuring cylinder is sufficient.

(*b*) Once the indicator has been added, the titration *must* be completed as soon as possible. It must not be left to stand. This is because the indicator is not stable once it has been added to the boiled and cooled digest.

(After Hora and Strepkov.)

5. Identification of simple sugars by chromatography (see p. 124)

Material. Fresh onion or spinach leaves.

Method. Place two batches of leaves in water and leave them in the dark for twelve and twenty-four hours; in this way they will become progressively starved. Place a third batch in the light to allow for the accumulation of higher carbohydrates.

After light and dark treatments make extracts of the material by squashing similar quantities of the leaves in a mortar with a little 50 per cent ethanol. Apply the extracts to filter-paper strips, sheets or thin-layer plates. The most satisfactory solvent is probably phenol. Full details are given on p. 164. In addition to identifying the spots, make an estimate of the relative amount of each substance found.

6. Polarimetric study of the inversion of sucrose (see pp. 125 and 126)

The Polarimeter

The polarimeter is an instrument designed to determine the degree certain substances are capable of rotating the plane of polarized light. It consists essentially of a source of monochromatic light, usually a sodium lamp or flame, secondly, a polarizing Nicol prism, thirdly, a tube, usually 20 cm. (2 dm.) long which contains the solution being investigated, and finally, an analysing prism. The instrument is provided with a *half-shade* device which makes analysis of the

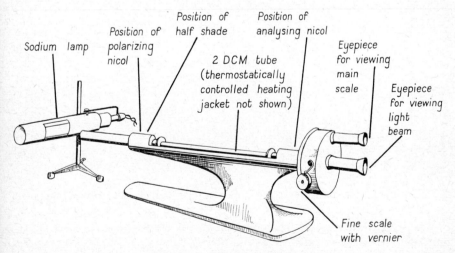

Fig. A.15. The polarimeter.

plane of rotation easier, the reading being taken when both sides of the field of view are equally illuminated. The plane of rotation is recorded on a vernier scale. A good instrument is also provided with a thermostatically controlled water jacket around the solution tube so that its temperature can be carefully regulated.

Setting up the polarimeter

First check the apparatus and see that the scale is on the zero mark; make adjustments if necessary. Make sure that the tube is clean and then fill it with the solution being examined, taking care to avoid bubbles. Do not screw down the end pieces of the tube too tight. Before placing the tube in the polarimeter check that it does not leak (and check again, at intervals, during the course of the experiment).

To determine the rate of inversion of sucrose at 20° C. using dilute acid

Prepare the following solution:
1. 20 gm. sucrose dissolved in 100 ml. distilled water.
2. 50 gm. N-hydrochloric acid.

Place these in an incubator at 20° C. for about half an hour.

Set up the heat jacket and pump system so as to provide a temperature of 20° C., and check the optical rotation of the 20 per cent sucrose. Knowing the specific rotation of sucrose at 20° C. to be $+66 \cdot 5°$, then the expected rotation can be calculated from the formula:

$$\left[\alpha\right]_D^{20} = \frac{100.\alpha}{l.c}$$

where $\left[\alpha\right]_D^{20}$ = Specific dextro rotation at 20° C.;

α = observed rotation;
l = length of tube in dcm.;
c = gm. sugar in 100 ml. water.

In this case the rotation should therefore be $+26 \cdot 6°$.

To determine the rate of the inversion of sucrose at 20° C. using the enzyme invertase

Dissolve 20 gm. of sucrose in 100 ml. $M/10\text{-}NaH_2PO_4$. This is incubated at 20° C. for half an hour and its rotation checked as above; 1 ml. of invertase concentrate (or as directed) is added to 20 ml. of the sucrose solution and the rotation recorded over a period of about half an hour. In this time the rotation should be reduced to zero.

Compare the graphs showing the rate of inversion using mineral acid and enzyme. By varying the temperature of the outside jacket (and temperature at which the materials are incubated), the temperature optimum for the inversion process may be found.

7. Extraction, purification and properties of starch phosphorylase (see p. 128)

Material. Most varieties of potato; peas (round varieties contain more starch phosphorylase than wrinkled varieties).

Method. Chop up and grind a small potato in a mortar together with a little ice-cold distilled water or phosphate buffer pH 7·0 (see p. 205) so as to produce about 10 ml. extract. Decant carefully and centrifuge at medium speed for about 5 minutes to clear the extract of starch grains. Check a drop of the supernatant for the presence of starch, using iodine. If necessary, centrifuge again. Pour off the supernatant and keep it cool until you are ready to carry out the next stage.

Make up 2 ml. of a 1 per cent solution of glucose-1-phosphate in distilled water. This must be freshly prepared.

Prepare two test-tubes with a 1 ml. glucose-1-phosphate in each. Add 1 ml. of the enzyme extract to the first tube and 1 ml. boiled extract to the second, shake the tubes. Test for the presence of starch immediately and at four-minute intervals by removing a drop of the liquid with a pipette and placing it on a white cavity tile together with a drop of iodine solution. Check that the original enzyme extract is starch free. How long does the starch take to be formed? Is the enzyme inactivated by boiling?

8. Identification of structural carbohydrates (see p. 128)

(a) CELLULOSE

Materials. The cell walls of most plants, particularly the collenchymatous or thickened walls found towards the outside of the cortex of some stems (e.g. *Helianthus*).

Test. This is a structural carbohydrate composed of complex chains of hexose units; it does not react with iodine unless first treated with concentrated sulphuric acid, when a blue-violet colour will be obtained (the Amyloid reaction). A better method is to treat a thin section of the material with Schultze's reagent,* which gives a blue colour with cellulose, but, like the Amyloid reaction, also stains any starch that may be present.

(b) HEMICELLULOSES

Materials. The cell walls of many seeds, e.g. the garden lupin and nasturtium (*Tropaeolum*).

Test. Superficially they resemble cellulose and they form thickenings on the inside of the cell wall, but they are easily hydrolysed by dilute acid and can be distinguished from cellulose in this way.

(c) LIGNIN

Materials. Woody tissues, xylem, fibres and sclerenchyma.

Test. This is the most complex structural carbohydrate and is derived from cellulose by conversion to various other complex organic molecules. It is stained bright magenta-red by phloroglucinol with HCl* and yellow by aniline sulphate.*

9. Identification of anthocyanin and anthoxanthin pigments (see p. 132)

Materials. Coloured flowers; leaves in autumnal colours.

A. *Chemical identification*

Grind a few petals or leaves in 80 per cent ethanol to obtain a general extract. Centrifuge or filter to remove debris and place in a separating funnel with an equal volume of petroleum ether (B.P. 100–120° C). Shake and then separate. Test the layers as follows:

(*a*) UPPER LAYER (petrol ether). If this is yellow, *carotenoids are present*. Add an equal volume of 95 per cent ethanol, shake and examine the distribution of colour. *Xanthophylls* are more soluble in the ethanol layer. *Carotenes* remain in the ether layer.

(*b*) LOWER LAYER (alcohol). If *coloured* this may contain both *anthocyanins* and *anthoxanthins*, if *colourless* no *anthocyanins* but possibly *anthoxanthins*.

These can be separated by dividing the solution into five test-tubes, having 2 ml. extract in each. Treat each as follows:

1. Add 4 drops 1 per cent dilute HCl to make the solution acid.
2. Leave (neutral).
3. Add 4 drops 1 per cent NaCO$_3$ to make the solution alkaline.
4. Add 4 drops 1 per cent NaOH to make the solution alkaline.
5. Make the solution alkaline with a few drops of 1 per cent Na$_2$CO$_3$, and then add 4 drops dilute FeCl$_3$.

The following table summarizes the colours that will be obtained with pure anthocyanins and anthoxanthins and with mixtures of the two:

	1 ACID	2 NEUTRAL	3 Na$_2$CO$_3$	4 NaOH	5 FeCl$_3$
AC	Red to mauve	Blue to mauve to pink	Blue	Blue	Slate–blue to purple
AX	Yellow or colourless	Yellow or colourless	Yellow	Yellow	Olive–yellow
AC + AX	Red	Pink	Green	Olive–brown–yellow	Olive–brown

There are no simple tests to distinguish the type of anthocyanidins present, but the following are frequently found, the colours being when the solution is neutral:

1.	*Pelargonidin*	Scarlet-red	5. *Cyanidin*	Purple
2.	*Peonidin*	Crimson	6. *Hirsutidin*	Blue
3.	*Malvidin*	Mauve	7. *Delphinidin*	Blue
4.	*Petunidin*	Purple		

B. *Chromatographic identification*

Full details of the filter-paper chromatography technique are given above on p. 164. An extract of the pigments is made in 80 per cent ethanol and the filter-paper spotted in the usual way; do not leave the extract, as it will fade. No developing spray is necessary.

Unfortunately it is extremely difficult to obtain reproducible results, and it is best to run the unknown extract against a known one such as can be obtained from the scarlet geranium (*Pelargonium*). In this case it is best to use a larger jar (see fig. A.6, p. 163), so that several different spots can be compared at the same time. The ratio of the R_f of the pigment to that of *Pelargonidin* should be a constant.

Intensification of the spots is possible by use of strong ammonia vapour. This will, of course, change the colour of the spot, but will, in addition, show up the presence of yellow Anthoxanthins, which have R_f values between 0·9 and 1·0.

10. Identification of lipids (see p. 136)

Unlike the carbohydrates, the lipids are insoluble in water but soluble in ether or chloroform. There are two main forms of lipids.

(a) OILS AND FATS

These are the triglycerides of fatty acids and are common food reserve substances.

Materials. Leaves of cocksfoot (*Dactylis glomerata*) and water mint (*Mentha aquatica*). Fruits of the olive (*Olea europaea*) and in the endosperm of many seeds such as the coconut (*Cocos nucifera*), sunflower (*Helianthus annuus*) and linseed or flax (*Linum usitatissimum*).

Test. Fat globules are stained by various Sudan stains.

(i) *Sudan III or IV.* (0·5 per cent in 70 per cent ethanol.) Wash excess stain from the material with 90 per cent ethanol. Fat globules are stained red.

(ii) *Sudan Black.* (1 per cent in 95 per cent ethanol or in propylene glycol; warm on a water-bath to dissolve the solid; filter before use.) This stain is useful for bulky tissues. Remove excess stain by washing the material with 70 per cent ethanol.

(iii) *Sudan Blue.* (0·5 per cent in ethanol; warm on a water-bath to dissolve the solid; filter before use.) This stain is useful for microscopic material. Remove excess stain by washing the material with distilled water.

(b) WAXES

These differ from the fats and oils in that the glycerol is replaced by monohydric or occasionally dihydric alcohols.

Materials. Leaves of most plants, particularly conifers, stems of cacti (*Cereus* spp.).

Test. These are not found in globules, but cover the epidermis of many plants. They are also stained by the Sudan stains.

(c) CUTIN AND SUBERIN

These are wax-like substances consisting of a mixture of various waxy condensation products of various fatty acids.

Materials. Cutin is found in the cuticular layer of many plants such as the *Rhododendron* and cherry-laurel. Suberin is the waterproofing substance in cork, and is common in the outer layers of old stems and roots.

Test. These substances also react with the Sudan stains.

APPENDIX TO CHAPTER 7

1. Investigation of the effect of auxins on the growth of cress roots and stems
2. Investigation of the effect of gibberellic acid on the growth of stems

1. Investigation of the effect of auxins on the growth of cress roots and stems (see p. 142)

Material. Cress seed.

Method. Sterilize twelve Petri dishes and surface sterilize 120 seeds by shaking them for three minutes in a 1 per cent solution of sodium hypochlorite. Wash them thoroughly in distilled water. Place a filter-paper in each Petri dish and moisten it with 5 ml. distilled water. Count ten seeds on to each filter-paper and place the Petri dishes in a dark incubator at 30° C. for forty-eight hours.

Weigh out carefully 0·1 gm. of both β-indolylacetic acid (IAA) and β-indolylbutyric acid (IBA), dissolve each separately in 1 litre of distilled water. This gives a solution containing 100 parts per million (p.p.m.) of auxin; it should be used within a few hours of being made up. Dilute the stock solution so as to provide the following working solutions:

(i) 10 p.p.m.
(ii) 5 p.p.m.
(iii) 1 p.p.m.
(iv) 0·1 p.p.m.
(v) 0·05 p.p.m.

The sixth Petri dish will contain distilled water.

After forty-eight hours remove the dishes and select the six most uniform, healthy seedlings in each dish, rejecting the less healthy; make careful, *separate*, measurements of the root and stem length of each seedling, the root length should be about 10 mm.

Add 7 ml. of the required auxin solution to each dish so as to provide a range of seedlings with different auxin concentrations. Replace in the incubator and after two days re-measure the stem and root lengths. Calculate the average increase in length for each auxin concentration and plot your results on a graph. Compare the stimulating and inhibiting effects of the two auxins.

2. Investigation of the effect of gibberellic acid on the growth of stems (sec p. 144)

Material. Cress seedlings (prepared as in exp. 1, above). Young plants of many species, e.g. peas, cabbages.

Method. This can be similar to exp. 1. Weigh out carefully 0·1 gm. of crystalline gibberellic acid and dissolve it in 1 litre of distilled water. This gives a solution containing 100 p.p.m. of gibberellic acid. This substance is not particularly soluble in water, but the latter should not be heated or rapid hydrolysis will occur. The solution should be used within a few hours of preparation. Dilute the stock solution so as to provide the following working solutions:

> (i) 10 p.p.m.
> (ii) 1 p.p.m.
> (iii) 0·1 p.p.m.

Distilled water and the stock solution of 100 p.p.m. should also be used. The remainder of the experiment is as described above.

Larger plants may be sprayed with the solutions and left longer before final measurements are made.

Appendix B.   Useful Reagents

Aceto-lacmoid. One per cent solution dissolved in 45 per cent acetic acid. Filter off undissolved solid after it has had some hours to dissolve. Add two drops of N-HCl to a watch-glassful of the stain before use. The stain deteriorates after about one month.

Aceto-orcein. One per cent solution dissolved in 45 per cent acetic acid. Filter off undissolved solid after it has had some hours to dissolve. The stain is used without HCl and deteriorates after about one month.

Alcohol. See *Ethanol*.

Aniline sulphate. One per cent solution dissolved in distilled water. Filter and acidify with a few drops of dilute sulphuric acid.

Baryta water (N/10 solution). Dissolve about 50 gm. of barium hydroxide and 15 gm. of barium chloride in 500 ml. of boiling distilled water. Allow the solution to cool with a tube of soda-lime corked into the neck of the flask. The excess barium hydroxide will crystallize out and the clear fluid may be siphoned off into a second vessel, from which carbon dioxide has been removed, without allowing the solution to come into contact with the outer air. Its strength will be about 0·35N. Add about a litre of freshly boiled distilled water, which has cooled under soda-lime, and standardize with N/10-HCl, using phenol phthalein (from James: *An Introduction to Plant Physiology*, by permission of the Clarendon Press, Oxford.)

Benedict's reagent.
> *Solution A.*: Weigh out 17·3 gm. copper sulphate and dissolve this in 150 ml. distilled water.
> *Solution B.*: Weigh out 173 gm. sodium citrate and 90 gm. anhydrous sodium carbonate. Dissolve these in 850 ml. distilled water and filter.
> Add solution A to solution B slowly, with constant stirring. The reagent does not deteriorate on standing.

Borate buffer. Take 5 gm. pure boric acid and place it in a 500-ml. flask. Add 100 ml. absolute alcohol and 350 ml. distilled water. Add 2·5 ml. bromocresol green and 2·5 ml. methyl red and adjust the pH to 5·0 (a reddish purple) using sodium hydroxide.

Brodie's fluid. Take 46 gm. pure sodium chloride, 10 gm. sodium tauroglycocholate and add distilled water to 1 l. To this add 1 gm. thymol dissolved in the smallest amount of alcohol then add 0·5 gm. of water-soluble eosin.

Buffers. See borate buffer, phosphate buffer.

Dinitrophenylhydrazine. Dissolve 0·1 gm. of 2:4-dinitrophenylhydrazine in dilute hydrochloric acid made by mixing 17 ml. concentrated hydrochloric acid with 20 ml. of distilled water. Warm on a water-bath to dissolve the solid. Dilute the cold solution to 100 ml. with distilled water. The reagent is dilute and is used for the qualitative identification of substances containing aldehyde or ketone groups, with which it forms brownish crystalline hydrazones.

Ethanol. Laboratory rectified spirit is about 95 per cent and is diluted as required.

Fehling's solution.

> *Solution A.:* 35 gm. of crystalline copper sulphate dissolved in 500 ml. of distilled water.
>
> *Solution B.:* 175 gm. of Rochelle salt (sodium potassium tartrate) and 50 gm. of sodium hydroxide dissolved in 500 ml. of distilled water.
>
> Equal quantities of these solutions to be mixed just before use.

Guaiacum solution. Dissolve a few pieces of guaiacum resin in 95 per cent alcohol so as to make a pale coffee-coloured solution. Use the solution freshly prepared.

Iodine. Dissolve 5 gm. of iodine crystals in 1 l. of a strong solution of potassium iodide.

Millon's reagent (Cole's version).

> *Solution A.* Mix 100 ml. of pure sulphuric acid with 800 ml. distilled water and carefully add 100 gm. of mercuric sulphate, filter and make up to 1 l.
>
> *Solution B.* 10 gm. of pure sodium nitrite dissolved in 1 l. of distilled water.

Nadis' reagent. Can be obtained commercially and is made from three solutions:

> *Solution 1.* Dimethyl-*p*-phenylene diamine solution.
>
> *Solution 2.* α-naphthol solution.
>
> *Solution 3.* Sodium carbonate solution.
>
> The reagent should be made up fresh using equal quantities of each solution.

Ninhydrin. Dissolve 0·2 gm. solid in 100 ml. *n*-butanol. It should be used freshly prepared.

***p*-anisidine hydrochloride.** Dissolve 1·5 gm. in 50 ml. *n*-butanol. The solution should be used freshly prepared.

Phenol phthalein. Dissolve 1 gm. in 100 ml. alcohol.

Phloroglucinol +HCl. Dissolve 1 gm. in 100 ml. alcohol and add a few drops of concentrated hydrochloric acid.

Phosphate buffer. Citric acid:Na_2HPO_4. pH 6·5.

> *Citric acid solution* 0·1M. Dissolve 10 gm. citric acid in 500 ml. distilled water.
>
> Na_2HPO_4 *solution* 0·2M. Dissolve 17·8 gm. $Na_2HPO_4.2H_2O$ in 500 ml. distilled water.
>
> Add 14·5 ml. citric acid to 35·5 ml. sodium phosphate. The buffer will then be about pH 6·5. Buffers at other pH values can be made using more or less of either reagent, but it is best to check the pH using a B.D.H. kit.

Pyrogallol. Take 10 gm. of sodium hydroxide and dissolve in 10 ml. distilled water. Add this solution to one made by adding 2 gm. of pyrogallic acid to 6 gm. of distilled water. Stopper firmly with a rubber bung.

Resorcinol + HCl. Dissolve 10 gm. resorcinol in 100 gm. acetone and add a few drops of concentrated HCl. The solution should be used freshly prepared.

Schultze's reagent. Dissolve 100 gm. of zinc in 300 ml. of pure HCl. Evaporate the solution down to 150 ml. During the evaporation a little extra zinc should be added. Take 12 gm. of potassium iodide and 0·15 gm. of iodine crystals and dissolve them in as little distilled water as possible. Mix the two solutions. If any precipitate forms the solution should be filtered through glass wool. Store in a dark, tightly stoppered bottle.

Sodium bicarbonate indicator

Preparation of stock solution. Dissolve 0·2 gm. of thymol blue and 0·1 gm. of cresol red in 20 ml. ethanol. Add 0·84 gm. of pure sodium bicarbonate to 900 ml. distilled water in a graduated flask. Add the dyes to this solution and make up to 1 litre. Take care to exclude dust and dirt.

Preparation of final indicator. Pipette 25 ml. of the stock solution into a 250 ml. graduated flask and make up the volume with distilled water. The colour of this indicator should be red. If it is orange or yellow, aspirate atmospheric air through the solution.

(After *Biology Teachers Guide*, Year III, Nuffield Science Teaching Project.)

Bibliography

A. GENERAL

ESAU, K. (1953). *Plant Anatomy.* New York, Wiley.
FOGG, G. E. (1963). *The Growth of Plants.* Harmondsworth, Penguin Books.
GABRIEL, M. L., and FOGEL, S. (1955). *Great Experiments in Biology.* Englewood Cliffs, New Jersey, Prentice-Hall.
JAMES, W. O. (1955). *Plant Physiology,* 5th edn. London, Oxford Univ. Press.
MEYER, B. S., ANDERSON, D. B., and BÖHNING, R. H. (1960). *Introduction to Plant Physiology,* 3rd edn. Princeton, New Jersey, Van Nostrand.
SKENE, M. (1955). *The Biology of Flowering Plants,* rev. edn. London, Sidgwick & Jackson.
SMITH, K. M. (1962). *Viruses.* London, Cambridge Univ. Press.
STANLEY, W. M., and VALENS, E. G. (1962). *Viruses and the Nature of Life.* London, Methuen.

B. CELL STRUCTURE

HURRY, S. W. (1965). *The Microstructure of Cells.* London, John Murray.
The Living Cell. *Scientific American,* **205**, No. 3, Sept. 1961.
MERCER, E. H. (1961). *Cells and Cell Structures.* London, Hutchinson Educational.
PICKEN, L. (1960). *The Organisation of Cells and other Organisms.* London, Oxford Univ. Press.
SWANSON, C. P. (1960). *The Cell.* Englewood Cliffs, New Jersey, Prentice-Hall.

C. WATER RELATIONS

BARON, W. M. M. (1967). *Water and Plant Life.* London, Heinemann.
MAXIMOV, N. A. (1929). *The Plant in Relation to Water.* Translated by R. H. Yapp. London, Allen & Unwin.
SOCIETY FOR EXPERIMENTAL BIOLOGY (1965). *The State and Movement of Water in Living Organisms.* S.E.B. Symposium No. 19. London, Cambridge University Press.
RUTTER, A. J. and WHITEHEAD, F. H. (1963). *The Water Relations of Plants.* Oxford, Blackwell.

D. PHOTOSYNTHESIS

BASSHAM, J. A., and CALVIN, M. (1957). *The Path of Carbon in Photosynthesis.* Englewood Cliffs, New Jersey, Prentice-Hall.
BUTT, V. S. (In press). *Photosynthesis.* Oxford, Blackwell.
FOGG, G. E. (1953). *The Metabolism of the Algae.* London, Methuen.

E. RESPIRATION

JAMES, W. O. (1953). *Plant Respiration.* London, Oxford Univ. Press.
STILES, W. and LEACH, W. (1960). *Respiration in Plants,* 4th edn. London, Methuen.

F. MINERAL NUTRITION

BEAR, P. E., *et al.* (1949). *Hunger Signs in Crops.* Washington, American Society of Agronomy.

HOAGLAND, D. R. (1944). *Lectures on the Inorganic Nutrition of Plants. Chronica Botanica.*

RUSSELL, SIR E. J. (1957). *The World of the Soil.* London, Collins.

RUSSELL, SIR E. J. (1961). *Soil Conditions and Plant Growth,* 9th edn. London, Longmans.

STEWART, W. D. P. (1966). *Nitrogen Fixation in Plants.* London, Athlone Press.

WALLACE, T. (1961). *Mineral Deficiencies in Plants.* London, H.M.S.O.

G. BIOCHEMISTRY

ANFINSEN, B. C. (1959). *The Molecular Basis of Evolution.* New York, Wiley.

BALDWIN, E. (1959). *Dynamic Aspects of Biochemistry,* 3rd edn. London, Cambridge Univ. Press.

FLORKIN, M. (1960). *Unity and Diversity in Biochemistry.* Oxford, Pergamon Press.

HARRISON, K. (1959). *A Guide-Book to Biochemistry.* London, Cambridge Univ. Press.

SCIENTIFIC AMERICAN READER (1955). *Physics and Chemistry of Plant Life.* London, Bell.

SZENT-GYÖRGYI, A. (1960). *An Introduction to Submolecular Biology.* New York, Academic Press.

THORPE, W. V. (1957). *Biochemistry for Medical Students.* London, Churchill.

H. CYTOLOGY AND GENETICS

DARLINGTON, C. D., and LA COUR, L. F. (1947). *The Handling of Chromosomes,* 2nd edn. London, Allen & Unwin.

——, and MATHER, K. (1949). *The Elements of Genetics.* London, Allen & Unwin.

FINCHAM, J. R. S. (1965). *Microbial and Molecular Genetics.* London, English Universities Press.

McLEISH, J., and SNOAD, B. (1958). *Looking at Chromosomes.* London, Macmillan.

SRB, A. M., and OWEN, R. D. (1959). *General Genetics.* San Francisco, Freeman.

WILLIAMS, W. (1959). The Control of Variation in Garden Plants. *Journal of the Roy. Hort. Soc.,* **84,** 7, p. 317.

I. HORMONES AND GROWTH

AUDUS, L. J. (1959). *Plant Growth Substances.* London, Leonard Hill.

WARDLAW, C. W. (1952). *Morphogenesis in Plants.* London, Methuen.

J. ECOLOGY

ASHBY, M. (1961). *Introduction to Plant Ecology.* London, Macmillan.

DAUBENMIRE, R. F. (1959). *Plants and Environment,* 2nd edn. New York, Wiley.

K. PRACTICAL TECHNIQUES

ABBOTT, D. and ANDREWS, R. S. (1965). *An Introduction to Chromatography*. London, Longmans.

ALLEN, R. A., MILLETT, R. J., and SMITH, D. B. (1959). *Radioisotope Data*. London, H.M.S.O.

Autoradiography. Kodak Data Sheet SC–10.

CONWAY, E. J. (1950). *Microdiffusion Analysis and Volumetric Error*, 3rd edn. London, Crosby Lockwood.

FAIRES, R. A., and PARKS, B. H. (1958). *Radioisotope Laboratory Techniques*. London,

HALE, L. J. (1958). *Biological Laboratory Data*. London, Methuen.

LOOMIS, W. E., and SHULL, C. A. (1937). *Experiments in Plant Physiology*. New York, McGraw-Hill.

McLEAN, R. C., and IVIMEY COOK, W. R. (1941). *Plant Science Formulae*. London, Longmans.

MEYER, B. S., and ANDERSON, D. B. (1955). *Laboratory Plant Physiology*, 3rd edn. Princeton, New Jersey, Van Nostrand.

MINER, H. A., *et al.* (1959). *Teaching with Radioisotopes*. Washington, U.S. Atomic Energy Commission.

VOGEL, I. A. (1951). *A Textbook of Practical Organic Chemistry, including Qualitative Organic Analysis*. London, Longmans.

—— (1951). *A Textbook of Quantitative Inorganic Analysis*, 2nd edn. London, Longmans.

—— (1958). *Elementary Practical Organic Chemistry*. London, Longmans.

L. USEFUL PERIODICALS

Annual Review of Plant Physiology
Discovery
Endeavour
Journal of Chemical Education
Journal of Ecology
Nature
New Biology (series terminated)
New Phytologist
School Science Review
Science Journal
Science News
Science Progress
Scientific American

Index

Figures in bold type are the main references